Weight Watchers

Made to Measure
Cook Book

D0507991

Made to Measure Cook Book

Healthy Eating for You and Your Family

Ann Page-Wood

Hodder & Stoughton
LONDON SYDNEY AUCKLAND

Frontispiece illustration: Tabbouleh (recipe on page 98)
Front cover photograph by Steve Lee
Back cover photographs by Clive Streeter

For information about the Weight Watchers classes contact: Weight Watchers UK Ltd, Kidwells Park House, Kidwells Park Drive, Maidenhead, Berkshire SL6 8YT. Telephone: (0628) 777077

British Library Cataloguing in Publication Data

Page-Wood, Ann
Weight Watchers Made to Measure Cookbook:
Healthy Eating for You and Your Family
I. Title
641.5

ISBN 0-340-57446-1 (cased)
ISBN 0-340-59060-2 (pbk)

Copyright © 1993 by Weight Watchers International Inc.

First published in Great Britain 1993
Weight Watchers ⊕ is the registered trademark of Weight Watchers International Inc. and is used under its control by the publisher

All rights reserved. No part of this publication may be reproduced or transmitted in any form or by any means, electronic or mechanical, including photocopying, recording, or any information storage and retrieval system, without either prior permission in writing from the publisher or a licence permitting restricted copying. In the United Kingdom such licences are issued by the Copyright Licensing Agency, 90 Tottenham Court Road, London WIP 9HE. The right of Ann Page-Wood to be identified as the author of this work has been asserted by her in accordance with the Copyright, Designs and Patents Act 1988.

Published by Hodder and Stoughton,
a division of Hodder and Stoughton Ltd,
Mill Road, Dunton Green, Sevenoaks, Kent YN13 2YA
Editorial Office: 47 Bedford Square, London WC1B 3DP

Designed by Behram Kapadia
Photography by Clive Streeter (full pages) and Simon Smith
Home Economist Ann Page-Wood
Weight Watchers Consultant Margaret Turner
Assisted by Celia Whiston
Photoset by Rowland Phototypesetting Ltd, Bury St Edmunds, Suffolk
Colour separations by Planway Ltd, London
Printed in Great Britain by
Hazells Books Ltd, Member of BPCC Ltd, Aylesbury, Bucks.

Contents

Introduction

Not that long ago a meal of 'meat and two veg' satisfied just about everyone but today we demand much more from food: a variety of tastes and well-balanced, nutritious meals that all the family will enjoy. Our busy lifestyles often leave us with little time to prepare meals and we look more and more for appetising recipes with practical cooking techniques that don't involve slaving for too long over a hot stove.

Weight Watchers believe that healthy eating should be easy and fun rather than a chore. To help it naturally become part of everyone's lifestyle we have put together this new MADE TO MEASURE COOKBOOK with over 250 recipes that are suitable for every kind of occasion.

During the past few years the importance of using top quality fresh foods has become evident. Much more emphasis has been placed on regularly eating more fresh fruit, vegetables and grains and fewer saturated fats, highly refined and processed foods, which contain less dietary fibre and relatively high proportions of hidden salt, sugar and fat.

For almost thirty years Weight Watchers have promoted healthy eating with sensible weight control. Following a healthy diet and achieving weight loss doesn't mean that any one food should be totally excluded, but merely restricted. The Weight Watchers Programme reflects current Government recommendations for a healthy way of eating and includes reducing the amount of fat and sugar that we eat, whilst increasing the amount of fibre and carbohydrates in our diets. It is for this reason that we recommend the following:

Eat no more than seven eggs in one week.

Remove all visible fat from meat before it is cooked.

Red meat should be grilled rather than fried because of its higher fat content.

When using fat for cooking always choose a product that is high in polyunsaturates.

Remove the skin from poultry either before or after cooking.

Limit the amount of red meat and cheese you eat each week to no more than a combined total of 14 ounces (420 g).

The Recipes

All the recipes in the Weight Watchers MADE TO MEASURE COOK BOOK are calorie counted for the weight conscious and are based on the Weight Watchers Programme. They are all easy to prepare. Each recipe has been given a preparation and cooking time, so that you know how long a recipe will take to make before you start cooking.

Breakfast is probably the most important meal of the day but it is the one meal that is often avoided by dieters. In the first section called *Breakfasts with a Boost* you will find enjoyable and quick meals that will help you to get your day off to a good start. If you are cooking for yourself then the recipes in our *Solo Selection* will be invaluable to you by way of contrast. We have included a section called *Guests are Coming* for those more formal occasions – or for those of you who like to entertain at home for friends as well as family. Our *Cold Creations* are deliciously refreshing and they require no cooking at all. While the recipes in *It's So Simple!* and *Meals in Minutes* will give you lots of ideas if you don't want to spend too much time in the kitchen. And, finally, the *Winter Warmers* section is just bulging with family favourites that everyone will be tempted to try.

We do hope you enjoy this new addition to the Weight Watchers range of cookery books. Now all the family can enjoy nutritious, healthy and balanced eating while you can still watch the calories.

Measurement Conversion Tables

There are many different tables used for converting imperial recipes to metric measures. All the recipes in this book have imperial and metric equivalents, either use one or the other, never mix the two. As one ounce equals 28.35 grams an exact conversion is not practicable for home booking and Weight Watchers use the following tables in their Programme.

Weights

½ oz	15 g
¾ oz	20 g
1 oz	30 g
2 oz	60 g
3 oz	90 g
4 oz	120 g
5 oz	150 g
6 oz	180 g
7 oz	210 g
8 oz	240 g
9 oz	270 g
10 oz	300 g
11 oz	330 g
12 oz	360 g
13 oz	390 g
14 oz	420 g
15 oz	450 g
1 lb	500 g
1 lb 8 oz	700 g

Volume

¼ teaspoon	1.25 ml spoon	
½ teaspoon	2.5 ml spoon	
1 teaspoon	5 ml spoon	
½ tablespoon	7.5 ml spoon	
1 tablespoon	15 ml spoon	
2 tablespoons	60 ml	1 fl oz
4 tablespoons	120 ml	2 fl oz
6 tablespoons	180 ml	3 fl oz
8 tablespoons	240 ml	4 fl oz
¼ pint	150 ml	5 fl oz
½ pint	300 ml	10 fl oz
¾ pint	450 ml	15 fl oz
1 pint	600 ml	20 fl oz

Oven Temperatures

Mark 1/2	250°F	120°C
1	275°F	140°C
2	300°F	150°C
3	325°F	160°C
4	350°F	180°C
5	375°F	190°C
6	400°F	200°C
7	425°F	220°C
8	450°F	230°C
9	475°F	240°C

Measurements

⅛ inch	3 mm
¼ inch	5 mm
½ inch	1.25 cm
1 inch	2.5 cm
1½ inch	4 cm
2 inch	5 cm

BREAKFASTS WITH A BOOST

Breakfast is probably the most important meal of the day. As it implies, it is the meal that 'breaks the fast' and will set you up for the day ahead. Yet it is the meal most frequently missed by people wishing to lose weight and can, therefore, result in pangs of hunger during the morning and nibbling before lunch. Even if you don't feel particularly hungry in the morning it is sensible to eat a light breakfast which will give you energy and set you up for the day ahead.

There are all kinds of breakfasts in this section, from cereals – one of the most popular breakfasts – and porridge, to Continental breakfasts of muffins and scones. The more substantial breakfasts, such as Egg, Tomato and Mushroom Toasted Cups (see page 24), are good for those late Sunday morning brunches, or for when you have a heavy day's work ahead of you and you'll only have time for a light snack at lunch.

Although this section is called Breakfasts with a Boost, the recipes may be enjoyed at any other time of the day. Some of the recipes make a delicious light lunch (see Mushrooms and Poached Eggs on Toast on page 21) or a satisfying dessert.

Cheese and Mustard Breadcakes

1 oz (30 g) bread
1 egg
¼ tsp Dijon or German mustard
3 tbs skimmed milk
1 oz (30 g) well-flavoured
  cheese, finely grated
1 tsp oil
2 slices of tomato to garnish
  (optional)

SELECTIONS PER SERVING:

½ Bread
½ Fat
1 Protein
5 Optional Calories

CALORIES PER
SERVING: 165

SERVES 2

PREPARATION AND COOKING TIME: 12 MINUTES

Break the bread into pieces and process in a liquidiser until breadcrumbs. With a fork lightly beat the egg together with the mustard and milk. Stir in the cheese and breadcrumbs and mix well.

Heat the oil in a large frying pan, spoon in the egg and bread mixture to make two circles. With the back of a spoon spread to make two 4–5 inch (10–12.5 cm) circles – if you don't have a large enough frying pan make one large breadcake and allow longer for cooking. Cook over a moderate heat for 3–4 minutes until set and when the edge of each breadcake is lifted slightly, the bottom is golden brown. Transfer the frying pan to a hot grill and cook for about 3 minutes until golden and slightly puffy. Arrange the tomato slices on top and return to the grill for a further 1–2 minutes.

Tip:

If your frying pan isn't non-stick and food tends to stick on the base spend 2–3 minutes 'proving' the pan (see page 163).

Illustration on previous page: Swiss Muesli and Banana and Honey Froth (see page 16)

Tofu Fruit Cream

1 × 200 g pack silken tofu,
  drained
6 oz (180 g) drained canned
  pineapple or crushed
  pineapple
1 tbs frozen concentrated
  orange juice, thawed
2 tbs low fat natural yogurt
½ oz (15 g) cornflakes or
  toasted cereal

SELECTIONS PER SERVING:

1 Fruit
1 Protein
30 Optional Calories

CALORIES PER
SERVING: 140

SERVES 2

PREPARATION: 5 MINUTES

NO COOKING REQUIRED

Place all the ingredients except the cornflakes in a liquidiser or food processor and process them to a smooth purée. Pour into a sundae glass and sprinkle with cornflakes or toasted cereal.

Tip:

The Tofu Fruit Cream can be covered and kept in the refrigerator overnight, and poured into a glass in the morning. If you prefer, omit the cereal and deduct 20 Optional Calories from the Selections.

Pineapple Porridge

1 oz (30 g) porridge oats
½ oz (15 g) oat bran
½ pint (300 ml) skimmed milk
4 oz (120 g) crushed pineapple
2 tsps honey
5 fl oz (150 ml) low fat natural
  yogurt
ground allspice to garnish
  (optional)

SELECTIONS PER SERVING:

½ Bread
½ Fruit
1 Milk
40 Optional Calories

CALORIES PER
SERVING: 205

SERVES 2

PREPARATION AND COOKING TIME: 8 MINUTES PLUS CHILLING OVERNIGHT

Place the porridge oats and oat bran in a saucepan, add the milk and bring to the boil stirring all the time. Boil for 4–5 minutes, stirring continuously, until the mixture is very thick.

Remove the saucepan from the heat and stir in the pineapple and honey, mix well then stir in 4–5 tbs yogurt. Spoon the mixture into two stemmed glasses and leave until cold. Cover the tops of the glasses and refrigerate overnight.

In the morning spoon on the remaining yogurt and sprinkle with allspice, if desired.

Variation:

The porridge may be made with half milk and half water, this will reduce the Milk Selection to ¾. (Total Calories per serving 180.)

Fruity Yogurt with Cottage Cheese

8 oz (240 g) cottage cheese
5 fl oz (150 ml) low fat natural
  yogurt
1 medium apple, chopped
3 oz (90 g) mixture dried dates
  and apricots, roughly
  chopped
¾ oz (20 g) walnut kernels,
  roughly chopped
1 tbs sunflower seeds

SELECTIONS PER SERVING:

1 Fruit
¼ Milk
1 Protein
45 Optional Calories

CALORIES PER
SERVING: 165

SERVES 4

PREPARATION: 5 MINUTES

NO COOKING REQUIRED

Blend the cottage cheese and the yogurt, mix in the fruits and walnuts then spoon into a serving bowl. Sprinkle over the sunflower seeds and serve.

Tip:

Some shops sell packets of broken walnut pieces, they are usually considerably cheaper than walnut halves.

Berry Parfait

4 oz (120 g) mixture of
  blueberries, raspberries or
  blackberries
5 fl oz (150 ml) low fat natural
  yogurt
1 tsp sugar
2 tsps desiccated coconut,
  toasted

SELECTIONS PER SERVING:

½ Fruit
½ Milk
20 Optional Calories

CALORIES PER
SERVING: 75

SERVES 2
PREPARATION: 5 MINUTES
NO COOKING REQUIRED

Divide the fruit between two serving glasses. Blend the yogurt with the sugar and half the coconut. Spoon the mixture over the fruit. Sprinkle with the remaining coconut and serve.

Variation:

Substitute half the yogurt with 2 oz (60 g) fromage frais. Selections will be: ½ Fruit, ¼ Milk, ½ Protein, 20 Optional Calories.

Banana Sunrise

1 tbs strawberry jam
1 medium banana
1 tsp lemon juice
2 oz (60 g) cottage cheese
½ tsp sunflower seeds

SELECTIONS PER SERVING:

2 Fruit
1 Protein
60 Optional Calories

CALORIES PER
SERVING: 200

SERVES 1
PREPARATION: 5 MINUTES
NO COOKING REQUIRED

Put the jam in a cup and stand it in a saucepan of simmering water until the jam becomes runny.

Cut the banana in half lengthways and brush with a little lemon juice. Add the rest of the juice to the jam.

Spread the cottage cheese down the middle of the banana, topping it with the runny jam. Sprinkle with sunflower seeds.

Tip:

You can warm the jam by putting it in the microwave for about 15 seconds.

Right: Berry Parfait

Swiss Muesli

1 oz (30 g) barley flakes
1 oz (30 g) rye flakes
1 oz (30 g) millet flakes
1 oz (30 g) jumbo oats
1½ oz (45 g) dried fruit (e.g.
    apple rings, apricots, prunes,
    dates or figs), chopped
½ oz (15 g) sultanas
2 tsps wheatgerm
1 tsp sesame seeds
2 tsps sunflower seeds
8 fl oz (240 ml) orange juice
To serve:
10 fl oz (300 ml) low fat natural
    yogurt
1 medium peach, chopped
4 oz (120 g) drained canned
    pineapple pieces

SELECTIONS PER SERVING:

1 Bread
1½ Fruit
½ Milk
20 Optional Calories

CALORIES PER
SERVING: 230

SERVES 4
PREPARATION: 5 MINUTES
NO COOKING REQUIRED
SOAKING TIME: OVERNIGHT

Mix together all the dry ingredients. Place in a non-metallic bowl, stir in the orange juice, cover and leave overnight.

When ready to serve, blend in the yogurt, peach and pineapple.

Variation:

The muesli may be divided into four single servings and stored in separate airtight containers. To serve one person; mix the dry ingredients with 4 tablespoons orange juice and soak overnight. In the morning stir in 5 tablespoons low fat natural yogurt and 2 oz (60 g) drained canned pineapple pieces. The Selections will remain the same.

Illustrated on pages 10/11

Banana and Honey Froth

½ pint (300 ml) skimmed milk
1 tsp wheatgerm
1 tsp honey
1 medium banana
ground cinnamon to garnish
    (optional)

SELECTIONS PER SERVING:

2 Fruit
1 Milk
30 Optional Calories

CALORIES PER
SERVING: 200

SERVES 1
PREPARATION: 5 MINUTES
NO COOKING REQUIRED

Process all the ingredients in a liquidiser until well blended and frothy. Pour into a tall glass and sprinkle with cinnamon, if desired.

Variation:

Substitute ½ pint (300 ml) buttermilk for the skimmed milk and half a medium mango for the banana. Selections will be: 1 Fruit, 1 Milk, 30 Optional Calories (Total Calories 185).

Mandarin Crunch

5 fl oz (150 ml) very low fat
    mandarin yogurt
2 oz (60 g) curd cheese or quark
1 medium mandarin or
    clementine, peeled and
    separated into segments
lemon juice
½ oz (15 g) crunchy or toasted
    breakfast cereal

SELECTIONS PER SERVING:

½ Bread
½ Fruit
1 Protein
100 Optional Calories

CALORIES PER
SERVING: 220

Gradually blend the yogurt into the curd cheese then stir in the mandarin or clementine. Add lemon juice to taste then spoon into a serving bowl. Sprinkle with the breakfast cereal and serve.

Tip:

Nutty Breakfast Crunch (see page 19) makes an ideal topping for this breakfast.

Banana Muffins

2 tbs oil
2 medium bananas
2 tbs clear honey
½ pint (300 ml) skimmed milk
8 oz (240 g) wholemeal self-
    raising flour
½ tsp bicarbonate of soda
½ tsp ground ginger
1 tbs wheatgerm

SELECTIONS PER SERVING:

½ Bread
½ Fat
55 Optional Calories

CALORIES PER
SERVING: 115

Illustrated overleaf

Pre-heat the oven to 200°C, 400°F, Gas Mark 6.

Grease twelve deep muffin tins with a little of the oil.

Mash the bananas with a fork then stir in the remaining oil, the honey and the milk.

Sieve the flour, bicarbonate of soda and ginger into a bowl. Tip in any bran remaining in the sieve and stir in the wheatgerm. Blend the banana and milk mixture into the dry ingredients then pour or spoon into the prepared tins.

Bake in the pre-heated oven for 25 minutes until well-risen and slightly cracked. Leave to cool for a few minutes then remove from the tins and cool on a wire rack.

Tip:

Freeze the muffins as soon as they are cold then remove them from the freezer as required. When thawed they may be warmed for a few minutes in an oven or for a few seconds in a microwave oven.

Nutty Breakfast Crunch

3 oz (90 g) hazelnut kernels, chopped
3 oz (90 g) rye flakes
3 oz (90 g) jumbo flakes
2 tsps wheatgerm
2 tsps sunflower seeds
2 tsps sesame seeds
½ oz (15 g) desiccated coconut
4 tsps oil
3 tbs clear honey
To serve per person:
1 oz (30 g) sultanas or raisins
2½ fl oz (75 ml) low fat natural yogurt

SELECTIONS PER SERVING:

1 Bread
1 Fat
1 Fruit
½ Milk
1 Protein
60 Optional Calories

CALORIES PER
SERVING: 345

SERVES 6

PREPARATION AND COOKING TIME: 1 HOUR

Pre-heat the oven to 140°C, 275°F, Gas Mark 1.

Mix all the dry ingredients together in a bowl. Heat the oil and honey in a small saucepan. Pour over the dry ingredients and stir well to coat. Spoon the mixture on to a large baking sheet and bake in the pre-heated oven for 45 minutes. Leave until cold then crumble into an airtight container.

To serve one person; mix together 1½ oz (45 g) Nutty Breakfast Crunch with the sultanas or raisins and yogurt.

Tip:

Try adding a few crunchy slices of dried banana to each serving but remember to weigh them and add the Optional Calories.

Left: Banana Muffins (page 17)
Right: Nutty Breakfast Crunch

Plain Scones

8 oz (240 g) plain flour plus
  2 tsps
1 tbs baking powder
¼ tsp salt
1½ oz (45 g) margarine
¼ pint (150 ml) skimmed milk

SELECTIONS PER SERVING:

1 Bread
1 Fat
15 Optional Calories

CALORIES PER
SERVING: 145

SERVES 8

PREPARATION AND COOKING TIME: 20 MINUTES PLUS 15 MINUTES
RESTING

Pre-heat the oven to 230°C, 450°F, Gas Mark 8.

Line a baking sheet with non-stick baking parchment.

Sieve 8 oz (240 g) flour together with the baking powder and salt into a bowl. Add the margarine (if possible margarine which has been stored in a freezer) and rub into the flour using your fingertips until the mixture resembles fresh breadcrumbs.

Make a well in the centre of the flour, add most of the milk and mix with a round-bladed knife to form a soft dough. Add more milk as necessary.

Dust the working surface and rolling pin with the remaining flour. Roll out the dough until ½–¾ inch (1.25–2 cm) thick. Using a 2½ inch (6.25 cm) pastry cutter, cut into 8 scones or 8 triangles. Place the scones on the lined tin and leave to stand for 15 minutes.

Brush the tops of the scones with the remaining milk then bake in the pre-heated oven for about 10 minutes or until well-risen and light golden brown. Cool for a few minutes on a wire rack and serve warm.

Tip:

Keep small amounts of margarine in the freezer ready for recipes where the fat has to be rubbed in.

Bran Muffins

8 oz (240 g) self-raising
  wholemeal flour
1 tsp baking powder
2 oz (60 g) oat bran
4 tbs oil
1½ oz (45 g) soft brown sugar
1 egg
12 fl oz (360 ml) skimmed milk

SELECTIONS PER SERVING:

½ Bread
1 Fat
55 Optional Calories

SERVES 12

PREPARATION AND COOKING TIME: 30 MINUTES

Pre-heat the oven to 200°C, 400°F, Gas Mark 6.

Sieve the flour and baking powder into a bowl, tip in any bran remaining in the sieve and stir in the oat bran.

Grease twelve deep non-stick muffin tins with a little of the oil.

Place the remaining oil, sugar, egg and milk in a jug and whisk with a fork until well combined. Pour into the dry ingredients and stir together.

CALORIES PER
SERVING: 145

Pour or spoon the mixture into the greased tins and bake in the pre-heated oven for 20 minutes until well-risen and slightly cracked on top. Leave to cool for a few minutes then remove from the tins and cool on a wire rack.

Tip:

Muffin tins are now sold in most department stores and kitchenware shops. Although this recipe can be baked in deep pattie tins the result will not be so successful and the Selections will have to be altered according to how many are made.

---

4 large cap-mushrooms, stalks
  removed
1½ tbs oil
2½ tbs tomato ketchup
4 eggs
salt
2 spring onions, finely chopped
4 × 1 oz (30 g) slices of bread
2 tbs very low fat spread

SELECTIONS PER SERVING:

1 Bread
1½ Fat
1 Protein
1 Vegetable
15 Optional Calories

CALORIES PER
SERVING: 230

Mushrooms and Poached Eggs on Toast

SERVES 4

PREPARATION AND COOKING TIME: 15 MINUTES

Place the mushrooms, smooth sides up, in a grill pan lined with foil. Brush with a little oil and cook under a moderate grill for 2–3 minutes.

While the mushrooms are cooking mix the remaining oil with the tomato ketchup. Turn the mushrooms over and spread evenly with the tomato ketchup and oil mixture then return to the grill and cook for a further 4–5 minutes.

Meanwhile poach the eggs: break the eggs into a pan of lightly salted, barely simmering water and stir round so the white is drawn round the yolk. Cook for 4 minutes.

Arrange the mushrooms on four serving plates, sprinkle with the spring onions, then remove the eggs with a draining spoon and place on top of each mushroom. Spread the bread with the very low fat spread, cut into triangles and serve with the mushrooms and eggs.

Variation:

If you prefer, poach the eggs in an egg poacher: grease each poaching cup with ¼ tsp margarine and cook over boiling water for 5 minutes. Add 10 Optional Calories per serving.

English Breakfast Platter

8 oz (240 g) cooked potatoes,
    preferably hot
1½ tbs margarine
salt
1½ tbs oil
2 oz (60 g) flour
4 tomatoes, halved
4 eggs
4 tbs skimmed milk
pepper

SELECTIONS PER SERVING:

1 Bread
1½ Fat
1 Protein
1 Vegetable
35 Optional Calories

CALORIES PER
SERVING: 265

SERVES 4

PREPARATION AND COOKING TIME: 25 MINUTES

Mash the potatoes with 1 tbs margarine and ½ tsp salt. Prove a griddle or heavy-based frying pan: generously sprinkle salt over and heat gently, tip out the salt then wipe thoroughly with a pad of kitchen paper. Heat a few drops of oil in the pan and wipe round once again.

Reserve 2–3 tsps flour, work the remainder into the potato mixture to give a stiff dough. Tip the dough on to a working surface and, using the remaining flour, roll out until about ¼ inch (5 mm) thick; cut into eight triangles.

Heat about 1 tsp oil on the griddle, place the scones on the griddle and cook over a low to moderate heat for about 4 minutes until golden then turn and cook the other side. While the scones are cooking cook the tomatoes under a moderate grill. Lightly whisk the eggs together with the skimmed milk, season with salt and pepper. Melt the remaining margarine over a moderate heat, pour in the egg mixture and cook stirring continuously until set to a creamy consistency. Arrange two halves of tomato, two scones and a quarter of the scrambled egg on each serving plate.

Tip One:

If possible make the potato scones with freshly cooked warm potatoes, if you have a microwave oven, cold potatoes can be warmed in a very short time.

Tip Two:

Varieties of potato differ in their quality, some are floury others waxy, therefore the amount of flour required to make the dough will vary. Measure the amount of flour you use and adjust the Selections and the calories accordingly. King Edward and Maris Piper potatoes are floury and ideal for mashing.

Right: English Breakfast Platter

Egg, Tomato and Mushroom Toasted Cups

8 × ½ oz (15 g) squares of thin
  white bread
2½ tbs margarine
2 eggs
4 tbs skimmed milk
salt and pepper
1½ oz (45 g) mushrooms,
  chopped
2 tomatoes, skinned, deseeded
  and chopped
1 tsp chopped fresh chives or
  parsley to garnish

SELECTIONS PER SERVING:

1 Bread
1½ Fat
½ Protein
¾ Vegetable
20 Optional Calories

CALORIES PER
SERVING: 195

SERVES 4

PREPARATION AND COOKING TIME: 25 MINUTES

Pre-heat the oven to 200°C, 400°F, Gas Mark 6.

Using a rolling pin roll each square of bread until very thin.

Melt 2 tbs margarine in a small saucepan. Use a little of the margarine to grease eight pattie tins. Brush one side of each bread square with a little of the margarine and press them gently into the pattie tins with the greased side uppermost. Set the saucepan aside. Bake the bread in the pre-heated oven for 12 minutes or until the edges are golden.

While the bread cups are cooking whisk the eggs and the milk until light and frothy. Season with a little salt and pepper. Melt the remaining margarine in a small saucepan, add the mushrooms and the tomatoes and stir over a low heat for about 3 minutes, seasoning to taste with a little salt and pepper.

Remove the bread cups from the pattie tins, arrange on warm serving plates and keep warm. Pour the eggs and milk into the saucepan containing the margarine left over after spreading the bread. Cook over a moderate heat, stirring all the time, until the eggs are just scrambled.

Spoon the scrambled eggs into four of the bread cups and the vegetables into the other four. Garnish with the chopped chives or parsley and serve.

Tip:

Never overcook scrambled eggs or the mixture will curdle and become solid lumps of egg in a watery liquid. Always remove the saucepan from the heat while the eggs are slightly runny.

Breakfast Stacks

2 oz (60 g) self-raising white flour
2 oz (60 g) self-raising wholemeal flour
6 oz (180 g) curd cheese
¼ pint (150 ml) skimmed milk
1 egg, lightly beaten
finely grated zest of ½–¾ lemon
1 tsp oil
2 tbs apricot conserve or jelly marmalade
lemon juice
½ tsp icing sugar

SELECTIONS PER SERVING:

1 Bread
1 Protein
50 Optional Calories

CALORIES PER
SERVING: 225

SERVES 4

PREPARATION AND COOKING TIME: 15 MINUTES

Prove a griddle or heavy-based frying pan: sprinkle with salt and heat gently then tip out the salt and wipe the pan with a wad of kitchen paper. Add a few drops of oil to the griddle and heat again, wipe round and set aside.

Sieve the flours into a bowl, tip any bran remaining in the sieve into the bowl. Place 2 oz (60 g) curd cheese in a jug, gradually blend in the milk and the egg. Add the lemon zest and stir well. Make a well in the flour and gradually beat in the milk mixture.

Heat the remaining oil on the greased griddle. Pour the batter on to the griddle to make four 3 inch (7.5 cm) pancakes. Cook until bubbles begin to appear and the undersides are light golden brown then turn over and cook the other sides. When the bases are light golden brown transfer to a warm plate, cover and repeat the procedure with the remaining mixture to make twelve pancakes.

Mix the remaining 4 oz (120 g) curd cheese with the apricot conserve or marmalade, add lemon juice to taste. Lay one of the pancakes on each of four serving plates, spread with a little of the curd cheese and conserve mixture. Cover with a second round and spread with the remaining conserve, top with the remaining pancakes. Sieve the icing sugar over and serve immediately.

Variation:

These stacks may be filled with a savoury spread and served for a snack meal, remember to adjust the Selections as necessary.

Meals in Minutes

All the meals in this section can be prepared and cooked in thirty minutes or less. Try to keep a variety of ingredients which have a long shelf life in your store cupboard for those times when you don't want to spend much time preparing a meal or when you've just run out of fresh ingredients. Cans of tuna, pilchards and sardines packed in brine, long-life milk, canned tomatoes and baked beans, tomato purée, pasta and rice can all be stored for several months, or even longer, and are always useful to have ready to use.

A freezer filled with wholemeal bread and rolls and a variety of vegetables is much more valuable to someone who is health-conscious, than a freezer containing shop-bought ready-made meals and desserts. If you have a microwave oven you can make many recipes in MADE TO MEASURE in advance when you have the time, then thaw them out and reheat them in the microwave when you are in a hurry and want a quick meal. Remember also that individual ingredients can be thawed in seconds in the microwave.

The recipes in this section are suitable for snacks, lunches or main meals.

2 × 1 oz (30 g) slices of bread
2 tsps low fat spread
½ medium apple, peeled, cored
   and sliced
1 oz (30 g) hard cheese (e.g.
   Cheddar, Gruyère,
   Emmenthal), grated

SELECTIONS PER SERVING:

2 Bread
1 Fat
½ Fruit
1 Protein

CALORIES PER
SERVING: 305

Toasted Cheese and Apple Sandwich

SERVES I

PREPARATION AND COOKING TIME: 10 MINUTES

Spread the slices of bread with the low fat spread. Arrange the apple slices over one slice of bread, sprinkle with the cheese, then sandwich with the remaining slice of bread. Cook under a hot grill until golden, turn and cook the other side.

Tip:

To cook the sandwich in a sandwich toaster brush the toaster with 1 teaspoon oil and add 1 Fat to the Selections. (345 Calories per serving.)

1 oz (30 g) slice of bread
1 tsp margarine
1 tbs finely chopped onion
1 tomato, skinned and finely
   chopped
1 oz (30 g) hard cheese (e.g.
   Cheddar, Gruyère,
   Emmenthal), grated

SELECTIONS PER SERVING:

1 Bread
1 Fat
1 Protein
1 Vegetable

CALORIES PER
SERVING: 210

Cheese and Onion Toasties

SERVES I

PREPARATION AND COOKING TIME: 10 MINUTES

Toast the bread and spread with the margarine. Sprinkle over the onion, and tomato, and top with the cheese. Place under a very hot grill until bubbling.

Variation:

Substitute the slice of bread with a 2 oz (60 g) chunk of French bread. Split the chunk of bread in half then toast and proceed as above. Increase the Bread Selections to 2. (290 Calories per serving.)

Illustration on previous page: Sardine Fish Cakes (page 51),
Cheesy Pasta with Broccoli (page 32) and Cheese Puffs with
Baked Beans (page 49)

French Toast with Mushrooms

1 oz (30 g) slice of bread
1 egg, lightly beaten
½ tbs oil
4–5 button mushrooms, sliced

SELECTIONS PER SERVING:

1 Bread
1½ Fat
1 Protein
½ Vegetable

CALORIES PER
SERVING: 200

SERVES 1

PREPARATION AND COOKING TIME: 10 MINUTES

Soak the bread in the beaten egg until it has absorbed all the liquid. Heat the oil in a non-stick frying pan then cook the bread for about 2 minutes on both sides until nicely golden.

Transfer to a serving plate and keep warm. Add the mushrooms to the pan and sauté quickly over a high heat, then spoon over the toast.

Tip:

If possible use a non-stick frying pan. You will be able to reduce the amount of oil required and reduce the Fat Selections accordingly.

Sweetcorn and Ham Fritters

½ oz (15 g) cooked ham,
    chopped
1 oz (30 g) self-raising flour
3 oz (90 g) well drained canned
    sweetcorn
1 egg, lightly beaten
dash of pepper sauce
2 tsps oil

SELECTIONS PER SERVING:

1 Bread
1 Fat
½ Protein
15 Optional Calories

CALORIES PER
SERVING: 190

SERVES 2

PREPARATION AND COOKING TIME: 15 MINUTES

Stir the ham with the flour then add the sweetcorn. Beat in the egg and season with a little pepper sauce.

Heat the oil in a small frying pan and when it is very hot spoon in the batter to make four fritters. Cook over a high heat until the undersides are golden, then carefully turn the fritters over and cook the other side.

Tip:

When making fritters or pancakes check the undersides are cooked before turning. This is easily done by very carefully lifting the edge with a palette knife or fish slice; if the base is golden the fritter may be turned, if not cook for another minute and check again.

Thick Bean and Vegetable Soup

2 tsps oil
8 oz (240 g) leeks, thinly sliced
1 large carrot, diced
2 sticks celery, sliced
6 oz (180 g) smoked tofu
16 fl oz (480 ml) tomato juice
12 oz (360 g) mixture of drained
    canned beans; liquid reserved
water or vegetable stock
2 oz (60 g) wholewheat pasta
    shells

SELECTIONS PER SERVING:

½ Bread
½ Fat
1½ Protein
2 Vegetable
15 Optional Calories

CALORIES PER
SERVING: 200

SERVES 4

PREPARATION AND COOKING TIME: 30 MINUTES

Heat the oil in a saucepan, add the leeks and stir round then cover the saucepan and cook gently over a low heat for 4–5 minutes. Stir in the carrot and celery, cover the saucepan and cook over a low heat for a further 4 minutes.

Liquidise the smoked tofu and tomato juice in a liquidiser or food processor. Pour the reserved liquid from the beans into a measuring jug and make up to ½ pint (300 ml) with water or weak vegetable stock.

Increase the heat under the vegetables and pour the tomato juice mixture, stock and beans into the saucepan. Bring to the boil, cover and simmer for 5–6 minutes.

Stir the pasta shells into the vegetables then cover the saucepan and cook for 8–10 minutes until the pasta and vegetables are cooked – do not overcook or the vegetables will be soft and the pasta will thicken the soup too much.

Tip:

Serve with 1½ oz (45 g) wedge of crusty French bread but remember to add 1½ Bread Selections. (320 Calories per serving.)

Left: Thick Bean and Vegetable Soup

Green Pea Soup

2 tsps margarine
1 onion, finely chopped
3 oz (90 g) potato, peeled and
    grated
½ pint (300 ml) chicken or
    vegetable stock
8 oz (240 g) frozen peas
salt and pepper

SELECTIONS PER SERVING:

1 Bread
1 Fat
½ Vegetable
30 Optional Calories

SERVES 2

PREPARATION AND COOKING TIME: 25 MINUTES

Heat the margarine in a small saucepan, add the onion and stir round then cover and cook gently over a low heat for 6–7 minutes.

Place the potato and stock in a separate saucepan and bring to the boil, reduce the heat and simmer until the potato is cooked.

Transfer the onion to the boiling potato and increase the heat. Add the frozen peas and bring to the boil. When the mixture is boiling reduce the heat, cover the saucepan and simmer for 10–12 minutes.

Continued overleaf

CALORIES PER
SERVING: 160

Transfer the vegetables and stock to a liquidiser or food processor and process to a purée. Pour the soup back into the saucepan, bring to the boil and season to taste. Pour the soup into warm bowls and serve.

Variation:

If you wish to serve only one portion, the remaining soup may be cooled and refrigerated or frozen. To make a nourishing snack, serve fruit and cheese at the same meal and add the additional Selections as necessary.

6 oz (180 g) pasta shapes
salt
8 oz (240 g) tiny broccoli florets
2 tsps margarine
1 clove garlic, finely chopped
10 oz (300 g) curd cheese
4 tsps finely grated Parmesan
    cheese

SELECTIONS PER SERVING:

1½ Bread
½ Fat
1 Protein
¾ Vegetable
25 Optional Calories

CALORIES PER
SERVING: 260

Cheesy Pasta with Broccoli

SERVES 4

PREPARATION AND COOKING TIME: 15 MINUTES

Cook the pasta in boiling salted water according to the packaging instructions.

Cook the broccoli in boiling water for about 8 minutes until bright green and a little crisp.

Heat the margarine in a saucepan and stir-fry the garlic for 2 minutes over a low heat, do not allow to brown. Add the curd cheese and reduce the heat as low as possible. Cook just long enough for the cheese to become runny.

Drain the broccoli, reserving the cooking liquid. Drain the pasta. Stir the pasta and broccoli into the curd cheese and thin with a little of the reserved cooking liquid.

Transfer the pasta mixture to four serving plates, sprinkle over the Parmesan cheese and serve.

Tip:

Take care not to overheat the curd cheese or it will separate. Although this will not alter the flavour the dish will lose its creamy texture.

Illustrated on pages 26/27

Cheese and Anchovy Toasts

3 oz (90 g) Cheddar cheese, grated
1 tbs margarine
½ tsp English or French mustard
2 tbs skimmed milk
3 drained canned anchovy fillets, chopped
2 × 1 oz (30 g) slices of bread

SELECTIONS PER SERVING:

1 Bread
1½ Fat
1½ Protein
10 Optional Calories

CALORIES PER
SERVING: 300

SERVES 2

PREPARATION AND COOKING TIME: 10 MINUTES

Put the cheese, margarine, mustard and milk into a small heavy-based saucepan. Add the anchovy fillets and stir well.

Toast the bread in a toaster or under a grill while gently heating and continuously stirring the cheese mixture.

Transfer the toast to two flameproof plates. Pour the melted cheese mixture over the toast and return to the grill until golden and bubbling.

Tip:

Serve with a colourful mixed salad.

Sesame Vegetable Stir-Fry

4 tsps sesame oil
4 oz (120 g) carrots, sliced
4 oz (120 g) celery, sliced
1 green pepper, deseeded and cut into thin strips
1 red pepper, deseeded and cut into thin strips
1 small onion, chopped
2 oz (60 g) cabbage or Chinese leaves, shredded
8 spring onions, cut into ½ inch (1.25 cm) diagonal slices
8 oz (240 g) water chestnuts
2 tbs toasted sesame seeds

SELECTIONS PER SERVING:

½ Bread
1 Fat
2 Vegetable
30 Optional Calories

CALORIES PER
SERVING: 115

SERVES 4

PREPARATION AND COOKING TIME: 20 MINUTES

Heat the oil in a wok or saucepan. Add the carrots, celery, peppers and onion and stir-fry over a medium heat for 4–5 minutes.

Add the remaining vegetables and water chestnuts and continue stir-frying until all the vegetables are hot but still crisp. Sprinkle with the sesame seeds and serve.

Tip:

If you are unable to buy toasted sesame seeds, toast your own; spread them evenly over a baking sheet or the base of a grill pan and while stir-frying the vegetables cook under a low to medium grill.

Smoked Fish Chowder

2 tsps margarine
1 onion, chopped
4 oz (120 g) potato, grated
1 pint (600 ml) skimmed milk
14 oz (420 g) smoked cod or
   haddock
bay leaf
salt and pepper
lemon juice
2 tbs chopped fresh parsley

SELECTIONS PER SERVING:

½ Fat
½ Milk
1½ Protein
¼ Vegetable
20 Optional Calories

CALORIES PER
SERVING: 190

SERVES 4

PREPARATION AND COOKING TIME: 30 MINUTES

Melt the margarine in a saucepan and stir-fry the onion for 3 minutes. Stir in the potato and milk, lay the smoked fish fillets on the mixture – if necessary cut the fillets into two or three pieces – add the bay leaf and simmer for 15 minutes or until the potato is cooked.

Using a fish slice lift the fish out of the saucepan and arrange on a plate. Remove the skin from the fish and flake into large pieces. Remove the bay leaf from the milk mixture then pour into a liquidiser or food processor. Add about half the fish and process until smooth.

Return the purée to the saucepan and season to taste with salt, pepper and lemon juice. Stir in the flaked fish and parsley and bring to the boil, stirring all the time. Serve immediately.

Tip:

Use long-life milk when simmering for more than a few minutes, it is less likely to burn.

Smoked Fish Chowder

Mackerel Pasta with Soured Cream

4 oz (120 g) pasta shapes
salt
2 tsps oil
1 onion, chopped
½ red pepper, deseeded and
　chopped
½ green pepper, deseeded and
　chopped
2 oz (60 g) fennel, sliced
10 oz (300 g) skinned smoked
　mackerel fillet, flaked
2 eggs, hard-boiled and chopped
6 tbs soured cream

SELECTIONS PER SERVING:

1 Bread
½ Fat
3 Protein
¾ Vegetable
45 Optional Calories

CALORIES PER
SERVING: 390

SERVES 4
PREPARATION AND COOKING TIME: 20 MINUTES

Cook the pasta in boiling salted water according to the packaging instructions.

Meanwhile heat the oil in a saucepan and stir-fry the onion and peppers for 4 minutes. Add the fennel, stir well, cover the saucepan and cook gently over a low to moderate heat for 3–4 minutes.

Add the mackerel, eggs, hot pasta and soured cream to the saucepan, stir until the mackerel is heated through and serve.

Tip:

To hard-boil eggs: place the eggs in a saucepan of cold water, bring to the boil and boil for 8 minutes. Then immediately plunge them in cold water and remove the shells – this should avoid a black line forming round the yolks.

Mackerel Pasta with Soured Cream

Simple Soufflé Omelette

salt and pepper
2 eggs, separated
1½ tsps margarine
1 oz (30 g) strong-flavoured hard cheese, e.g. mature Cheddar, Parmesan; finely grated

SELECTIONS PER SERVING:

1½ Fat
3 Protein

CALORIES PER SERVING: 280

SERVES 1

PREPARATION AND COOKING TIME: 10 MINUTES

Add a little pepper to the egg yolks in one bowl and mix with a fork.

Add a pinch of salt to the egg whites in a clean bowl and whisk until peaking.

Melt the margarine in a non-stick 7 inch (17.5 cm) frying pan over a low heat.

Using a metal spoon fold the whisked egg whites into the yolks. Increase the heat under the frying pan, add the egg mixture, and cook gently over a moderate to high heat for 2 minutes. Sprinkle on the cheese. Meanwhile pre-heat the grill.

Ease the edge of the omelette from the frying pan using a palette knife. When the underside is golden brown transfer the pan to the grill and cook for a minute, or less, until beginning to brown. Fold in half and serve immediately.

Tip:

Some shops sell pre-grated Parmesan cheese which can be more economical. Do not use the dried packaged variety, it does not have the same pungent flavour.

Potato and Parsnip Omelette

3 oz (90 g) potato
3 oz (90 g) parsnip, grated
1 oz (30 g) onion, grated
2 eggs
2 oz (60 g) feta cheese, crumbled
1 tbs oil

SELECTIONS PER SERVING:

1½ Fat
½ Bread
2 Protein
¼ Vegetable
20 Optional Calories

SERVES 2

PREPARATION AND COOKING TIME: 25 MINUTES

Grate the potato on to a clean cloth, roll up the cloth and squeeze tightly to remove as much liquid as possible. Transfer to a bowl. Mix in the parsnip and onion.

Lightly beat the eggs, add the cheese and stir into the vegetables.

Heat the oil in a 8–9 inch (20–22.5 cm) frying pan. Spoon the mixture into the pan and press down evenly using the back of a spoon. Cook over a low heat for 15 minutes.

CALORIES PER
SERVING: 275

Pre-heat the grill on its highest setting, remove the frying pan from the heat and place under the grill, cook for 4–5 minutes until lightly golden. Cut in half and slide on to two serving plates.

Tip:

While the omelette is cooking prepare a crisp mixed salad to serve with your meal.

1 oz (30 g) tagliatelle
salt
8 oz (240 g) mixture of carrot
 and calabrese broccoli, cut
 into 1½ inch (4 cm) lengths,
 broccoli heads divided into
 small florets
1½ tsps sesame oil
1 clove garlic, finely chopped
1 spring onion, finely chopped
1 oz (30 g) cooked ham, cut into
 strips
2 eggs
¼ pint (150 ml) skimmed milk
dash of pepper sauce
2 tsps grated Parmesan cheese

SELECTIONS PER SERVING:

1 Bread
1½ Fat
½ Milk
3 Protein
3 Vegetable
20 Optional Calories

CALORIES PER
SERVING: 390

Tagliatelle with Ham and Vegetables

SERVES 1
PREPARATION AND COOKING TIME: 20 MINUTES

Cook the tagliatelle in boiling salted water according to the packaging instructions.

Boil the carrot and broccoli in salted water for 3 minutes, drain well.

Meanwhile heat the oil in a saucepan and stir-fry the garlic and spring onion for 1–2 minutes. Add the ham, carrot and broccoli and stir-fry for a further 2 minutes.

Using a fork, lightly whisk the eggs together with the milk in a mixing bowl and season with a little salt and pepper sauce, add the hot drained tagliatelle. Pour the tagliatelle and sauce into the vegetables. Stir over a low heat until the sauce thickens, spoon on to a serving plate and sprinkle with the Parmesan cheese.

Tip:

Sesame oil has a very strong nutty flavour. It can be replaced with another oil such as groundnut or sunflower oil.

Spaghetti alla Carbonara

8 oz (240 g) spaghetti
salt
3 large eggs
4 tbs double cream
5 tbs skimmed milk
pepper
3 oz (90 g) cooked ham,
   chopped
1 oz (30 g) Parmesan cheese,
   finely grated
1 oz (30 g) Cheddar cheese,
   finely grated
2 tsps olive oil
1 onion, finely chopped
1 tbs chopped fresh parsley to
   garnish

SELECTIONS PER SERVING:

2 Bread
½ Fat
2 Protein
¼ Vegetable
35 Optional Calories

CALORIES PER
SERVING: 460

SERVES 4

PREPARATION AND COOKING TIME: 20 MINUTES

Cook the spaghetti in slightly salted boiling water according to the packaging instructions.

Meanwhile, using a fork whisk the eggs together with the cream and milk, season well with pepper then mix in the ham and cheeses.

Heat the oil in a saucepan or wok and stir-fry the onion for 5 minutes until soft.

Drain the cooked spaghetti and tip into the saucepan or wok, add the egg mixture and stir over a very low heat until the egg mixture thickens.

Divide the spaghetti between four warm serving bowls, sprinkle with parsley and serve.

Tip:

To reduce the cost of this recipe use 2 oz (60 g) mature Cheddar cheese instead of the mixture of Parmesan and Cheddar cheeses and replace the double cream with single cream. The Selections remain the same (but total number of Calories will be reduced to 395 per serving).

Spaghetti alla Carbonara

Prawn Curry

3 cardamom pods
¼ tsp ground coriander
½ tsp ground cumin
¼ tsp cayenne
¼ tsp turmeric
1½ tsps oil
¼ inch (5 mm) slice ginger,
    finely chopped
½ clove garlic, finely chopped
1 small onion, finely chopped
2 tsps tomato purée
5 tbs water
3 oz (90 g) peeled prawns

SELECTIONS PER SERVING:

1½ Fat
1½ Protein
½ Vegetable

CALORIES PER
SERVING: 165

SERVES 1

PREPARATION AND COOKING TIME: 20 MINUTES

Split the cardamom pods, remove the seeds and lightly crush them with the back of a spoon. Mix together with the coriander, cumin, cayenne and turmeric.

Heat the oil in a small saucepan, add the ginger and garlic and stir over a low heat for 1 minute – taking care not to burn. Add the onion and stir-fry for 3–4 minutes. Stir in the spices. Blend in the tomato purée then stir in the water and prawns. Bring to the boil, reduce the heat and simmer very gently for 5–6 minutes, stirring occasionally.

Variation:

To make a filling meal put 1½ oz (45 g) long grain rice on to cook before starting this recipe. The rice and Prawn Curry should be ready to serve at the same time. Add 1½ Bread Selections to the meal (making a total of 310 Calories per serving).

Prawn Curry

Fish Supper

SERVES 2

PREPARATION AND COOKING TIME: 25 MINUTES

10 oz (300 g) skinned cod or
  haddock fillet, about ¾ inch
  (2 cm) thick
4 tsps margarine
2½ oz (75 g) carrot, cut into
  very thin 1½ inch (4 cm)
  lengths
2 oz (60 g) celery, cut into very
  thin 1½ inch (4 cm) lengths
2 oz (60 g) leek, cut into very
  thin 1½ inch (4 cm) lengths
4 tbs weak stock
salt and pepper
1 oz (30 g) fresh breadcrumbs
1 oz (30 g) Gruyère or
  Emmenthal cheese, grated

SELECTIONS PER SERVING:

½ Bread
2 Fat
2½ Protein
1 Vegetable

CALORIES PER
SERVING: 290

Cut the fish in half across the grain.

Melt 2 teaspoons margarine in a small saucepan, add the prepared vegetables and stir over a moderate heat until they become limp. Add the stock, a little salt and pepper and cover. Cook gently over a low heat for 6 minutes until just cooked.

Spoon the hot vegetables into a shallow flameproof dish, make two dips in the vegetables and lay the fish fillets in them. Dot the fish with the remaining margarine and place under a moderately hot grill for about 8 minutes.

Mix the breadcrumbs with the grated cheese and scatter over the fish, return to the grill and increase the heat as high as possible. Cook until the cheese has melted and the breadcrumbs turned golden.

Variation:

If you wish, use smoked cod or haddock but omit the salt.

Ham and Egg Cocottes

SERVES 2

PREPARATION AND COOKING TIME: 20 MINUTES

½ tsp margarine
2 oz (60 g) cooked ham,
  chopped
2 tsps chopped fresh chives
2 eggs
2 tbs single cream

SELECTIONS PER SERVING:

2 Protein
40 Optional Calories

CALORIES PER
SERVING: 320

Pre-heat the oven to 180°C, 350°F, Gas Mark 4.

Grease two small ramekins with the margarine. Divide the ham between the ramekins. Sprinkle the chives over the ham and make a slight dip in the centre of each ramekin.

Break an egg into each dip, pour over the cream and transfer the ramekins to a baking tin half filled with steaming hot water. Bake in the pre-heated oven for 15 minutes.

Tip:

While the cocottes are cooking, toast 2 × 1 oz (30 g) slices of bread and make a mixed salad with 1 tomato, 2 sticks celery, 2 spring onions and a few crisp lettuce leaves. Spread each slice of toast with 1 teaspoon margarine. The Selections would be: 1 Bread, 1 Fat, 2 Protein, 1 Vegetable and 40 Optional Calories (470 Calories per serving).

Tofu and Vegetables with Dhal

4 tsps oil

1½–2 tsps finely grated fresh ginger

½ small onion, finely chopped

1 tsp ground coriander

3 oz (90 g) split red lentils

finely grated zest of ¼ lemon

½ pint (300 ml) vegetable stock

¼ tsp turmeric

½ tsp ground cumin

6 oz (180 g) firm tofu, cut into ½ inch (1.25 cm) cubes

7 tbs boiling water

1 leek, thinly sliced

3 oz (90 g) carrot, cut into 1½ × ¼ inch (4 cm × 5 mm) pieces

5–6 oz (150–180 g) cauliflower, divided into small florets

salt and pepper

3–4 tsps lemon juice

SELECTIONS PER SERVING:

1½ Bread
2 Fat
1 Protein
2½ Vegetable

CALORIES PER
SERVING: 305

SERVES 2

PREPARATION AND COOKING TIME: 35 MINUTES

Heat 2 teaspoons oil in a saucepan, add the fresh ginger and onion and stir-fry for 2–3 minutes. Stir in ½ teaspoon coriander then add the lentils, lemon zest and stock – do not add salt. Bring to the boil, stir well then cover and cook gently over a low heat for 20 minutes, stirring occasionally until cooked and thick.

Heat the remaining oil in a saucepan, add the turmeric, cumin and remaining coriander and stir well. Mix in the tofu and stir-fry for 3–4 minutes. Add 6–7 tablespoons boiling water, the leek, carrot and cauliflower and return to the boil. Add a little salt, cover tightly and cook gently over a moderate heat for 12 minutes until the vegetables are cooked but crisp. Cook for 1–2 minutes uncovered until the water has almost evaporated.

Arrange the tofu and vegetables on a warm serving plate. Season the dhal with a little salt and pepper and add lemon juice to taste. Spoon the dhal over the vegetables and serve.

Tip:

Double the amount of dhal could be made then half served with the tofu and vegetables and half frozen for future use. When reheated on the hob it may be necessary to add 2–3 tablespoons of water, but if covered and reheated in a microwave oven no additional liquid should be required.

Frankfurter Supper

3 oz (90 g) pasta spirals or
    shapes
salt
2 tsps oil
1 onion, chopped
½ green pepper, deseeded and
    cut into half circles
2 oz (60 g) button mushrooms,
    sliced
1 tomato, skinned and chopped
4 oz (120 g) frankfurters, cut
    into 1 inch (2.5 cm) lengths
good pinch of powdered
    mustard
2½ fl oz (75 ml) low fat natural
    yogurt

SELECTIONS PER SERVING:

1½ Bread
1 Fat
¼ Milk
2 Protein
1¾ Vegetable

CALORIES PER
SERVING: 340

SERVES 2

PREPARATION AND COOKING TIME: 20 MINUTES

Cook the pasta in lightly salted boiling water according to the packaging instructions.

Meanwhile heat the oil in a wok or saucepan and stir-fry the onion and green pepper for 4–5 minutes. Add the mushrooms, tomato, frankfurters and mustard and stir well. Cover the wok or saucepan and cook gently over a moderate heat for 4–5 minutes, stirring from time to time. Remove the mixture from the heat and blend in the yogurt.

Drain the pasta, stir together with the frankfurter mixture and serve.

Tip:

Some pre-packed frankfurters have to be cooked for 4 minutes so read the packaging and if necessary cook while preparing the vegetables.

Frankfurter Supper

Herby Beans Topped with Garlic Bread

2 tsps oil
1 large onion, finely chopped
2 tbs vegetable purée
15 oz (450 g) canned chopped
    tomatoes
1 tsp dried basil
¼–½ tsp chilli sauce
1 tbs soy sauce
salt
2 lb 4 oz (1.2 kg) mixture of
    drained canned beans e.g.
    kidney, haricot; liquid from
    the cans reserved
4 oz (120 g) French bread
4 tsps margarine
1 clove garlic, crushed

Herby Beans Topped With Garlic Bread

SERVES 4

PREPARATION AND COOKING TIME: 30 MINUTES

Heat the oil in a saucepan, add the onion and stir round then cover the saucepan and cook gently over a low heat for 5–6 minutes. Stir in the vegetable purée, canned tomatoes, basil, chilli sauce and soy sauce, season to taste with salt, cover and bring to the boil.

Drain the liquid from the cans of beans and reserve ¼ pint (150 ml), if necessary make up with water. Pour the liquid and the beans into the saucepan, return to the boil and then simmer for 15 minutes.

Continued overleaf

SELECTIONS PER SERVING:

1 Bread
1½ Fat
3 Protein
1¾ Vegetable

CALORIES PER
SERVING: 300

Cut the bread into eight slices. Mash the margarine with the garlic then spread over the bread.

Spoon the bean mixture into a flameproof dish, arrange the slices of bread on top, margarine side uppermost, and grill under a high heat until golden.

Tip:

To save time toast the garlic bread while the beans are cooking and arrange over the beans before serving.

4 oz (120 g) easy-cook long
    grain rice
salt
1 tsp sesame oil
1 leek, thinly sliced
½ red pepper, deseeded and cut
    into thin 1 inch (2.5 cm)
    lengths
3 eggs
2½ tsps light soy sauce
1 tsp margarine
1 large courgette, cut into thin
    1 inch (2.5 cm) lengths
2–3 tsps chopped fresh
    coriander
1 oz (30 g) roasted peanuts

SELECTIONS PER SERVING:

2 Bread
1½ Fat
2½ Protein
1¾ Vegetable

CALORIES PER
SERVING: 400

Vegetable and Egg Savoury Rice

SERVES 2

PREPARATION AND COOKING TIME: 25 MINUTES

Cook the rice in lightly salted boiling water according to the packaging instructions.

Meanwhile heat the sesame oil in a saucepan, add the leek and red pepper and stir well then cover and cook gently over a low heat for 4 minutes.

Using a fork beat the eggs together with the soy sauce.

Melt the margarine in a small frying pan – if possible a non-stick frying pan – add the egg mixture and cook over a high heat, drawing the cooked edge of the omelette towards the centre so the runny uncooked mixture runs to the edge of the pan.

Stir the courgette and coriander into the leek and pepper mixture, cover and cook gently over a low heat for 3–4 minutes.

Cut the omelette into 1–1½ inch (2.5–4 cm) squares.

Stir the omelette and vegetables into the hot rice, add the peanuts and serve.

Variation:

The peanuts may be omitted and the Selections reduced to:
2 Bread, 1 Fat, 1½ Protein, 1¾ Vegetable, giving a total of 360 Calories per serving.

Speedy Tuna and Tomato Pizza

2 tbs oil plus 2 tsps
1 small onion, thinly sliced
6 oz (180 g) self-raising flour
salt
8 oz (240 g) canned chopped
   tomatoes
1 tbs tomato purée
¼–½ tsp dried oregano
3 oz (90 g) drained canned tuna,
   flaked
4 anchovy fillets, halved
10 small black olives
8 capers
1½ oz (45 g) Mozzarella cheese,
   grated

SELECTIONS PER SERVING:

1½ Bread
2 Fat
½ Protein
1 Vegetable
30 Optional Calories

CALORIES PER
SERVING: 300

SERVES 4

PREPARATION AND COOKING TIME: 25 MINUTES

Heat 2 teaspoons of the oil in a saucepan, add the onion and stir round then cover the pan and cook gently over a low heat for 5–6 minutes, stirring occasionally.

While the onion is cooking prepare the base. Reserve 2 teaspoons flour, sieve the remainder into a mixing bowl and add a good pinch of salt. Stir in 1 tablespoon oil and 3–4 tablespoons water to make a soft dough.

Dust a working surface and rolling pin with the reserved flour and roll out the dough to form a 7–7½ inch (17.5–19 cm) circle.

Heat 1 tablespoon oil in an 8½ inch (21.25 cm) frying pan, lay the dough in the frying pan and cook over a moderate heat for 4–5 minutes until the base is golden brown.

Stir the tomatoes into the saucepan with the onion and boil rapidly for 2–3 minutes until thick.

Carefully turn the dough circle over and cook the other side. While the pizza base is cooking arrange the topping on top. Spread with the tomato purée and sprinkle over the oregano. Spoon the onion and tomato mixture evenly over then scatter the tuna, anchovies, olives and capers over the top. Finally, sprinkle on the cheese.

When the underside of the pizza is golden transfer the frying pan to a very hot grill and cook until the cheese is bubbling.

Variations:

Add 1 finely chopped clove garlic, a few rings of chilli and 2 oz (60 g) sliced button mushrooms to the onion, stir-fry for 4–5 minutes then add the tomatoes and continue as above. Add ¼ Vegetable Selection per serving.
or
Omit the tuna, anchovies and capers and substitute 3 oz (90 g) cooked sliced frankfurters. Add one Protein to the Selections and reduce the Optional Calories to 20. Each serving will be 355 Calories.

Speedy Tuna and Tomato Pizza *illustrated overleaf*

Chicken and Avocado Pitta Parcels

2 × 1½ oz (45 g) pitta breads
1 tbs blue cheese dressing
2 tbs low fat natural yogurt
2 oz (60 g) cooked chicken,
    chopped into small pieces
1½ oz (45 g) seedless white
    grapes, halved
1½ oz (45 g) avocado, chopped
1 oz (30 g) beansprouts
2–3 lettuce leaves

SELECTIONS PER SERVING:

1½ Bread
1½ Fat
1 Protein
¼ Vegetable
25 Optional Calories

CALORIES PER
SERVING: 270

SERVES 2
PREPARATION: 5 MINUTES
NO COOKING REQUIRED

Using a sharp knife split along one side of each pitta bread.

In a small bowl stir the blue cheese dressing together with the yogurt then add the chicken, grapes, avocado and beansprouts. Mix all the ingredients well to coat with the dressing.

Shred the lettuce leaves and place in each pitta bread then spoon the chicken mixture on top.

Tip:

Pitta bread splits more easily if slightly warm; either place in a warm oven for a few minutes or if you own a microwave oven heat for a few seconds before cutting.

Chicken and Avocado Pitta Parcels *illustrated on previous page*

Blue Cheese Pears

2 medium pears
lemon juice
2 oz (60 g) Danish blue cheese
4 oz (120 g) fromage frais
few salad leaves
2 tsps chopped fresh chives
4 chive flowers to garnish
    (optional)

SELECTIONS PER SERVING:

½ Fruit
1 Protein
¼ Vegetable

CALORIES PER
SERVING: 95

SERVES 4
PREPARATION: 10 MINUTES
NO COOKING REQUIRED

To prepare the pears, cut each pear in half lengthways, scoop out the core with a teaspoon and remove the stringy strands which attach the core to the stalk. Brush each pear half with lemon juice.

Crumble the Danish blue cheese into a bowl, mash well. Gradually mix in the fromage frais. Transfer the cheese mixture to a piping bag fitted with a ½ inch (1.25 cm) fluted nozzle.

Arrange the salad leaves on four serving plates, sprinkle over the chives and lay each pear half on top, cut-half facing upwards. Pipe the cheese into the cavity left by the core and down towards the stalk end.

Garnish each plate with a chive flower and serve.

Variation:

To make a quick snack serve each pear half with a 2 oz (60 g) wedge of crusty bread and a mixed salad but remember to add 2 Bread Selections. The Calories per serving will then become 230.

Cheesy Puffs with Baked Beans

1 egg, separated
1 oz (30 g) smoked cheese, finely grated
2 tbs skimmed milk
1 tsp oil
pinch of salt
6 oz (180 g) canned baked beans

SELECTIONS PER SERVING:

1 Bread
½ Fat
1 Protein
5 Optional Calories

CALORIES PER
SERVING: 190

SERVES 2

PREPARATION AND COOKING TIME: 15 MINUTES

Place the egg yolk in a mixing bowl with half to three-quarters of the cheese. Add the milk and mix well.

Spoon the oil into a large frying pan and place over a very low heat.

Add a pinch of salt to the egg white in a clean bowl and whisk until peaking then fold into the egg yolk mixture.

Increase the heat under the frying pan and spoon the mixture into the pan to make two puffs. Cook over a moderate heat for about 3 minutes until the bases of the puffs are golden brown.

While the puffs are cooking spoon the baked beans into a small saucepan, place over a low heat, stirring occasionally.

Sprinkle the remaining cheese over each puff and place the frying pan under a hot grill. Cook for about 3 minutes until puffy and golden brown.

Spoon the hot baked beans on to two warm serving plates, transfer the puffs to the plates and serve immediately.

Variation:

To make a more substantial meal serve with a selection of vegetables.

Illustrated on pages 26/27

Two Cheese Pasta

6 oz (180 g) pasta shapes
salt
1½ tbs butter
4 spring onions, cut into thick
    diagonal slices
1 red pepper, deseeded and cut
    into thin strips
1 green pepper, deseeded and
    cut into thin strips
12 oz (360 g) curd cheese
4 oz (120 g) Gorgonzola cheese
4 tomatoes, sliced
3–4 tsps chopped fresh parsley
    to garnish

SELECTIONS PER SERVING:

1½ Bread
2½ Protein
1½ Vegetable
40 Optional Calories

CALORIES PER
SERVING: 430

SERVES 4
PREPARATION AND COOKING TIME: 20 MINUTES

Cook the pasta in slightly salted boiling water for 12 minutes.

Meanwhile heat the butter in a saucepan, add the prepared vegetables and stir-fry for 4–5 minutes. Reduce the heat as low as possible then add the curd cheese and crumble in the Gorgonzola cheese and stir round for 1 minute. Remove the saucepan from the heat.

Drain the hot pasta and stir into the cheese sauce. Pile the pasta into a warm bowl or on to a warm serving plate. Arrange the tomatoes round the pasta, sprinkle over the parsley and serve.

Tip:

Do not overheat the cheese; cook over a very low heat until the curd cheese thins and the Gorgonzola cheese has melted, if cooked too long the curd cheese will separate.

Spaghetti with Smoked Haddock

4 oz (120 g) spaghetti
8 oz (240 g) smoked haddock
    fillets
¼ pint (150 ml) skimmed milk
1 lemon
4–6 spring onions, roughly
    chopped
a few sprigs of parsley
paprika

SELECTIONS PER SERVING:

2 Bread
¼ Milk
1½ Protein
¼ Vegetable

SERVES 2
PREPARATION AND COOKING TIME: 20 MINUTES

Cook the spaghetti in a saucepan of boiling water – do not add salt as the fish is salty.

Remove the skin and any bones from the fish then put it in a saucepan and pour in the milk.

Using a potato peeler cut a 2½ inch (6.25 cm) thin strip of zest from the lemon. Add to the fish together with the spring onions and two or three sprigs of parsley. Cover the saucepan and place over a low heat. Simmer for 8–10 minutes until the fish is cooked.

CALORIES PER
SERVING: 320

Transfer the cooked fish, milk, lemon zest, parsley and spring onions to a liquidiser or food processor and process to form a purée. The purée will not be smooth but will resemble well-cooked scrambled eggs.

Drain the spaghetti, mix with the haddock purée and transfer to two serving bowls. Dust with a little paprika. Cut the lemon into wedges and serve with the pasta.

Variation:

For a richer meal liquidise the hot fish with an egg and 3 tablespoons cream and mix into the hot spaghetti. The Selections would then be: 2 Bread, ¼ Milk, 2 Protein, ¼ Vegetable, 45 Optional Calories (and the meal 425 Calories per serving).

---

8 oz (240 g) cooked potatoes
1 tbs creamed horseradish
1 tsp lemon juice
5 oz (150 g) well-drained
   canned sardines
2 oz (60 g) fromage frais
1 large spring onion, finely
   chopped
salt and pepper
¾ oz (20 g) dry breadcrumbs
1 tbs skimmed milk
4 tsps margarine

SELECTIONS PER SERVING:

1½ Bread
2 Fat
3 Protein
30 Optional Calories

CALORIES PER
SERVING: 390

*Illustrated on
pages 26/27*

Sardine Fish Cakes

SERVES 2
PREPARATION AND COOKING TIME: 20 MINUTES

Mash the potatoes together with the horseradish and lemon juice. Add the fish and fromage frais and mash well. Mix in the spring onion then season to taste with salt and pepper.

Divide the mixture into four and shape each quarter into a round about 1 inch (2.5 cm), or a little more, thick.

Spread the dry breadcrumbs on a small piece of greaseproof paper. Brush one side of a fish cake with a little milk and press into the breadcrumbs. Brush the top of the cake with a little milk and turn to coat with the crumbs. Raise the edges of the paper to spread the crumbs evenly as necessary. Repeat with the remaining fish cakes.

Heat the margarine in a frying pan, add all the fish cakes and cook over a moderate heat for about 7–8 minutes, turning once, until golden brown on both sides.

Tip:

These fish cakes may be made in advance and stored in the refrigerator. If you wish to freeze them, lay them on a tray and open freeze then wrap in a double layer of aluminium foil, or store in a suitable container.

Cheesy Macaroni with Peppers

5 oz (150 g) macaroni
salt
1 oz (30 g) margarine
6 oz (180 g) frozen peppers
   (diced or strips)
1½ oz (45 g) flour
1 pint (600 ml) skimmed milk
2 oz (60 g) Parmesan cheese,
   finely grated
4 oz (120 g) Cambozola, rind
   removed, cut into small cubes
pepper

SELECTIONS PER SERVING:

1½ Bread
1½ Fat
½ Milk
1½ Protein
½ Vegetable
10 Optional Calories

CALORIES PER
SERVING: 430

SERVES 4
PREPARATION AND COOKING TIME: 25 MINUTES

Cook the macaroni in boiling salted water for 10–12 minutes then drain.

While the macaroni is cooking heat the margarine in a saucepan, add the peppers and cover. Cook over a low heat for about 6 minutes, stirring occasionally, until the peppers are soft. Sprinkle in the flour and stir well until evenly combined. Gradually blend in the milk.

Bring the pepper sauce to the boil, stirring all the time, boil for 2 minutes. Stir the macaroni into the sauce and simmer for 8–9 minutes, stirring frequently to prevent sticking.

Remove the creamy macaroni from the heat and add the cheese, stir until the cheese has completely melted. Season to taste with salt and pepper. Serve with a crisp mixed salad.

Variation:

Add a few diced cooked vegetables, ham or smoked tofu to the macaroni sauce. Remember to add the additional Selections and Calories.

Pepper Eggs

1 tsp oil
1 onion, quartered and thinly
   sliced
1 red pepper or ½ red and
   ½ green pepper, quartered,
   deseeded and thinly sliced
¼ tsp chilli sauce
1 large tomato, skinned and
   roughly chopped
salt
2 eggs

SELECTIONS PER SERVING:

½ Fat
1 Protein
2 Vegetable

SERVES 2
PREPARATION AND COOKING TIME: 20 MINUTES

Heat the oil in a frying pan, add the onion and pepper and stir round then cover the pan with a saucepan lid and leave to steam for 4 minutes. Stir in the chilli sauce then add the tomato and a little salt. Stir well then cover the pan and cook gently over a low heat for 10 minutes. Add a few more drops of chilli sauce if desired.

Make two dips in the pepper and onion mixture, break the eggs into them and cover the pan once again. Cook gently over a low heat for about 3 minutes or until the eggs are cooked to your liking.

CALORIES PER
SERVING: 110

Variation:

If desired replace the chilli sauce with 1½ teaspoons tomato ketchup. This will not alter the Selections.

11–12 oz (330–360 g)
  aubergine, cut into 1½ inch
  (4 cm) cubes
salt
2 tsps oil
1 clove garlic, chopped
2 onions, cut into ½ inch
  (1.25 cm) cubes
6 oz (180 g) easy-cook long
  grain rice
½ tbs chilli sauce
8 oz (240 g) canned chopped
  tomatoes
½ tbs tomato purée
3 tbs water
6–7 oz (180–210 g) flat
  mushrooms, cut into ½ inch
  (1.25 cm) cubes
1½ oz (45 g) watercress,
  roughly chopped

SELECTIONS PER SERVING:

1½ Bread
½ Fat
3 Vegetable
5 Optional Calories

CALORIES PER
SERVING: 200

Mushroom and Aubergine Pilaff

SERVES 4

PREPARATION AND COOKING TIME: 30 MINUTES

Place the aubergine in a sieve and sprinkle liberally with salt, leave for about 10–15 minutes to allow some of the bitter juices to drip away.

Heat the oil in a saucepan, add the garlic and onions and stir well then cover the saucepan and cook over a low heat for about 8 minutes.

Cook the rice according to the packaging instructions in slightly salted boiling water.

Blend the chilli sauce, chopped tomatoes, tomato purée and water together then stir into the onion mixture and bring to the boil. Rinse the aubergine and add to the saucepan with the mushrooms and watercress, cover then simmer for 15 minutes.

Drain the rice and arrange in a ring round a serving dish, spoon the vegetables into the centre and serve.

Variation:

For a more substantial meal add 6 oz (180 g) cubed tofu or drained canned kidney beans to the vegetables and add ½ Protein Selection (making a total of 240 Calories per serving).

Tuna and Vegetable Pie

1 lb (480 g) cooked or uncooked
   potatoes
1 tbs margarine
1 onion, grated
8 oz (240 g) frozen mixed
   vegetables
1 oz (30 g) flour
½ pint (300 ml) skimmed milk,
   plus 1–2 tbs
1 tsp anchovy essence
8 oz (240 g) well-drained
   canned tuna
4 oz (120 g) fromage frais
salt and pepper
2 tsps low fat spread

SELECTIONS PER SERVING:

1 Bread
1 Fat
¼ Milk
1½ Protein
1 Vegetable
25 Optional Calories

CALORIES PER
SERVING: 295

Left: Tuna and Vegetable Pie

SERVES 4

PREPARATION AND COOKING TIME: 30 MINUTES

If using uncooked potatoes, peel, cut into 2 inch (5 cm) chunks and boil in lightly salted water for about 15 minutes until cooked.

Melt the margarine in a saucepan and stir in the onion. Cover the saucepan and cook over a low heat for 10 minutes, stirring occasionally.

Cook the frozen vegetables according to their packaging instructions.

Sprinkle the flour over the onion, stir well then blend in ½ pint (300 ml) milk, bring to the boil stirring all the time and boil for 2 minutes. Stir in the anchovy essence. Drain the vegetables and flake the tuna then stir into the sauce.

Mash the potatoes, add the fromage frais and the remaining milk and mash until smooth. Season with salt and pepper to taste.

Spoon the tuna and vegetable sauce into a flameproof dish. Spread the potato mixture evenly on top and roughen with a fork. Dot the low fat spread over the potato and grill for 3–4 minutes until golden.

Variation:

Chicken and Courgette Pie. Substitute the tuna with 4 oz (120 g) diced cooked chicken, replace the mixed vegetables with diced courgettes and use 2 teaspoons vegetable purée instead of anchovy essence. The Selections remain the same.

Mexican Tacos

2 tsps oil
1 small onion, finely chopped
good pinch of hot chilli powder
6 oz (180 g) drained canned
   kidney beans; 2 tbs liquid
   reserved
1 tsp tomato purée
2 × 1 oz (30 g) taco shells
1 oz (30 g) cheese, grated
1–2 lettuce leaves (optional)

SERVES 2

PREPARATION AND COOKING TIME: 10 MINUTES

Heat the oil and stir-fry the onion for 4–5 minutes. Add the chilli powder, kidney beans, the reserved liquid and the tomato purée and continue cooking over a low heat while mashing with a potato masher. When the beans are thoroughly mashed continue cooking, stirring with a wooden spoon.

Continued overleaf

SELECTIONS PER SERVING:

½ Bread
1 Fat
1½ Protein
¼ Vegetable

CALORIES PER
SERVING: 265

Spoon the refried beans into the taco shells, sprinkle with the cheese. Shred the lettuce and arrange on top of the cheese.

Variation:

If you prefer, a cold filling can be served in the taco shells, for example, mix 3 oz (90 g) cubes of cooked pork or chicken with 2 oz (60 g) chopped avocado and a mixture of 1 tbs yogurt and 2 tsps low-calorie mayonnaise. Spoon into the taco shells and top with a little shredded lettuce. The Selections would be: ½ Bread, 1½ Fat, 1½ Protein, ¼ Vegetable, 5 Optional Calories (305 Calories per serving).

12 oz (360 g) potatoes
salt
2 tsps margarine
1–2 tbs skimmed milk
1 oz (30 g) cheese, grated
pepper
6 oz (180 g) canned baked beans
2 eggs

SELECTIONS PER SERVING:

1½ Bread
1 Fat
2½ Protein
5 Optional Calories

CALORIES PER
SERVING: 375

Poached Egg with Beans and Mashed Potato

SERVES 2
PREPARATION AND COOKING TIME: 25 MINUTES

Cook the potatoes in lightly salted boiling water. Drain then mash with the margarine and milk. Mix in the cheese, season with salt and pepper.

Using a ½ inch (1.25 cm) fluted nozzle, pipe the potato round the edge of a small shallow flameproof dish. Place the dish under a moderate grill to brown the potato while preparing the rest of the meal. (If you prefer, spoon the potato in four heaps round the side of the dish, roughen the surface then grill.)

Heat the baked beans gently in a small saucepan.

Pour about 3 inch (7.5 cm) boiling water into another small saucepan, add ½ teaspoon salt and heat until simmering. Break the eggs into the saucepan and very gently stir round so the white surrounds the yolk. Poach until cooked to suit your taste.

Spoon the hot beans into the flameproof dish and lay the poached eggs on top. Serve immediately.

Variation:

If preferred, use ½ teaspoon margarine to grease two cups in an egg poacher and cook the eggs in the cups over simmering water. Add 10 Optional Calories to each serving, bringing the Calories per serving up to 385.

Liver and Vegetable Stir-Fry

1 tbs oil

2 oz (60 g) celery, cut into sticks 1½ inch (4 cm) long and ½ inch (1.25 cm) wide

2 oz (60 g) carrot, cut into sticks 1½ inch (4 cm) long and ½ inch (1.25 cm) wide

2 oz (60 g) swede, cut into sticks 1½ inch (4 cm) long and ½ inch (1.25 cm) wide

4 oz (120 g) mixture of broccoli and cauliflower, stalks thinly sliced and florets divided into small clusters

3 spring onions, cut into 1 inch (2.5 cm) thick lengths

3 × 2 oz (60 g) slices lamb's liver

2½ fl oz (75 ml) low fat natural yogurt

1 tsp Dijon mustard

SELECTIONS PER SERVING:

1½ Fat
¼ Milk
2½ Protein
1¾ Vegetable

CALORIES PER
SERVING: 265

SERVES 2

PREPARATION AND COOKING TIME: 20 MINUTES

Heat 2 teaspoons oil in a saucepan or wok, add the celery, carrot and swede and stir-fry for 1–2 minutes then cover the saucepan and cook over a low heat for 4–5 minutes. Add the broccoli, cauliflower and spring onions to the saucepan or wok, stir round, cover and steam for 5 minutes.

While the vegetables are cooking heat the remaining oil in a small, if possible non-stick, frying pan. When the oil is very hot add the liver and cook for about 1 minute then turn and cook the other side for 1 minute. Transfer to a chopping board and cut into thin lengths, about the same size as the celery and carrot.

Increase the heat under the vegetables, add the liver and cook for 2–3 minutes until the liver is just cooked – do not overcook, or it will be tough.

Mix together the yogurt and Dijon mustard, stir into the liver and vegetables and serve.

Variation:

Replace the swede with parsnip and add 1 teaspoon tomato or vegetable purée to the yogurt. Add 20 Optional Calories to the meal, the Calories per serving would then be 275.

SOLO SELECTION

There is no reason why cooking for one should be a monotonous task. Cooking can and should be enjoyable and it doesn't need to take much of your time. Spend time planning your meals and choose recipes which suit your particular taste and which use the ingredients you have bought. All the recipes in Solo Selection are for single portions which create an added advantage: there's never any food left over for a second helping!

If you live or eat alone it's all too easy to slip into bad habits and rely on quick, convenience food and TV dinners. The main danger here is that these foods tend to be very refined and contain a high proportion of fat, yet they don't have the fibre and nutritional value that is necessary for a well balanced diet.

Although this section contains all single portion recipes, you will find many other recipes in this book which serve one person. Breakfasts with a Boost and Meals in Minutes have a variety of single portion recipes. Alternatively the majority of these recipes can be doubled or trebled to feed more people – or the extra servings can be frozen in single portions for later use, saving both time and money.

Vegetable Moussaka

3 oz (90 g) aubergine, thinly
   sliced
salt
1 oz (30 g) green lentils
½ tbs oil
1 clove garlic, finely chopped
1½ oz (45 g) onion, chopped
1½ oz (45 g) red pepper,
   deseeded and chopped
1 small carrot, diced
3 oz (90 g) canned pease
   pudding
1 tomato, skinned and roughly
   chopped
5 tbs (75 ml) vegetable stock or
   water
1 tsp tomato purée
1–2 tsps soy sauce
1 egg
3 tbs low fat natural yogurt
1½ oz (45 g) Parmesan cheese,
   grated

SELECTIONS PER SERVING:

2 Bread
1½ Fat
¼ Milk
2½ Protein
3¼ Vegetable
5 Optional Calories

CALORIES PER
SERVING: 515

SERVES 1

PREPARATION AND COOKING TIME: 1 HOUR

Pre-heat the oven to 180°C, 350°F, Gas Mark 4.

Place the aubergine in a sieve and sprinkle liberally with salt, set aside.

Place the green lentils in a saucepan, cover with cold water, bring to the boil and boil rapidly for 10–15 minutes.

Heat the oil in a saucepan, add the garlic, onion and red pepper and stir-fry for 2–3 minutes. Add the carrot, cover the saucepan and cook over a low heat for 5–6 minutes. Blend in the pease pudding, tomato, stock or water, tomato purée and soy sauce. Drain the lentils and add to the saucepan. Bring to the boil stirring all the time. Reduce the heat, cover the saucepan and leave to simmer for 7–8 minutes.

Rinse the aubergine well, transfer to a steamer and cook over the lentils and vegetables for the last 4–5 minutes of their cooking time.

Spoon the lentils and vegetables into a small pie dish or 5 inch (12.5 cm) soufflé dish. Arrange the aubergine slices over the top. Beat together the egg and yogurt, stir in the Parmesan cheese then pour over the aubergine. Bake in the pre-heated oven for 30 minutes.

Tip:

You can keep the remaining aubergine in a plastic bag pierced with several holes stored in the refrigerator for later use.

Illustration on previous page: Minced Beef and Haricot Bean Pie
(page 80)

Crunchy Vegetable Stir-Fry

For the marinade:

½ tbs tomato purée
1 tbs soy sauce
1 tbs water
1 clove garlic, crushed

For the stir-fry:

3 oz (90 g) tofu, cut into 1 inch (2.5 cm) cubes
3 oz (90 g) baby corn on the cob
1½ oz (45 g) carrot, cut into thin strips
1½ oz (45 g) mangetout, topped and tailed
2 oz (60 g) courgette, sliced
1 tsp oil
¼ inch (5 mm) slice ginger, finely chopped
½ small onion, chopped
½ small red pepper, deseeded and cut into strips
1 oz (30 g) beansprouts
½ oz (15 g) split almonds

SELECTIONS PER SERVING:

1 Bread
1½ Fat
2 Protein
2½ Vegetable

CALORIES PER SERVING: 295

SERVES 1

PREPARATION AND COOKING TIME: 22 MINUTES PLUS MARINATING TIME

Place the tomato purée, soy sauce, water and garlic in a screw-top jar and shake well to mix the ingredients.

Lay the tofu in a small non-metallic dish and pour over the marinade. Leave in the cool for at least one hour, stirring occasionally if possible.

Cook the corn in boiling water for 3 minutes, add the carrots and boil for 1 minute. Add the mangetout and courgette and cook for a further 1 minute.

Heat the oil in a saucepan or wok, add the ginger, onion and red pepper and stir-fry for 3–4 minutes. Blend in the tofu, marinade and all the blanched vegetables and stir-fry for about 4 minutes or until all the vegetables and tofu are piping hot. Add the beansprouts and split almonds and continue stir-frying for 2 minutes.

Tip:

The tofu may be prepared in advance and left to marinate for several hours. Cover the dish and leave in the refrigerator until required.

Tomato and Vermicelli Soup

1 tsp margarine
½ medium onion, chopped
1 small carrot, chopped
8 oz (240 g) tomatoes, chopped
¼ pint (150 ml) weak vegetable
    stock
sprig of basil
salt and pepper
½ oz (15 g) vermicelli noodles

SELECTIONS PER SERVING:

½ Bread
1 Fat
3 Vegetable

CALORIES PER
SERVING: 145

SERVES I

PREPARATION AND COOKING TIME: 45 MINUTES

Melt the margarine in a saucepan and stir-fry the onion for 3 minutes. Stir in the carrot, tomatoes and stock, add the basil and bring to the boil. Reduce the heat, cover the saucepan and simmer for 20 minutes.

Process the tomato mixture in a liquidiser or food processor to a purée. Sieve the purée, pressing against the side of the sieve with a spoon to extract as much juice as possible.

Reheat the soup, adjust the seasoning and add the noodles. Cover the saucepan and simmer for about 5 minutes or until the noodles are cooked.

Left: Crunchy Vegetable Stir-Fry (page 61) and Gooseberry and Vanilla Fool (page 85)

Right: Tomato and Vermicelli Soup

Vegetable Curry Soup

1 tsp oil
1½ oz (45 g) onion, finely
    chopped
1 oz (30 g) celery, finely
    chopped
1½ oz (45 g) carrot, finely
    chopped
approximately 1½ tsps curry
    powder
½ tbs flour
¼ pint (150 ml) vegetable stock
1 clove garlic
lemon juice
salt
1½ tbs double cream
2 tbs skimmed milk

SELECTIONS PER SERVING:

1 Fat
1½ Vegetable
70 Optional Calories

CALORIES PER
SERVING: 170

SERVES 1
PREPARATION AND COOKING TIME: 30 MINUTES

Heat the oil in a small saucepan and stir-fry the onion for 1–2 minutes. Add the celery and carrot. Blend in the curry powder and flour, gradually stir in the stock. Remove the papery skin from the garlic clove and thread it on to a cocktail stick. Add the garlic to the stock and bring to the boil, stir well then cover the saucepan and leave over a low heat for 15–20 minutes until the vegetables are cooked.

Remove the garlic clove then process the soup in a liquidiser or food processor until smooth. Pour back into the saucepan and reheat.

Remove from the heat and add a little lemon juice and salt to taste. Blend the cream with the milk then stir into the soup and serve.

Variation:

To make a filling snack meal serve the soup with a 1 oz (30 g) wedge of crusty wholemeal bread but remember to add the 1 Bread Selection (increasing the Total Calories per serving to 250).

Courgette and Brie Stuffed Tomato

1 × 4 oz (120 g) tomato
2 oz (60 g) courgette, grated
1 small stick celery, finely
    chopped
1 spring onion, finely chopped
1 oz (30 g) blue Brie (weighed
    with rind removed)
1 tbs low fat natural yogurt

SELECTIONS PER SERVING:

1 Protein
2½ Vegetable
10 Optional Calories

CALORIES PER
SERVING: 135

SERVES 1
PREPARATION: 12 MINUTES
NO COOKING REQUIRED

To prepare the tomato: cut a thin slice from the top, then use a teaspoon to remove the seeds and flesh. Turn the tomato upside down to drain.

Place the courgette in a cloth and squeeze to remove as much liquid as possible. Mix together with the celery and spring onion.

Mash the blue Brie in a small bowl, blend in the yogurt. Stir into the courgette, celery and spring onion. Spoon the stuffing into the tomato, press down firmly and pile the remaining mixture on top. Lay the slice of tomato on top and serve.

Variation:

2 oz (60 g) curd cheese seasoned with a little pepper sauce may be used in place of the blue Brie and yogurt. Delete the 10 Optional Calories. (Total Calories per serving 95.)

Egg Florentine

7–8 oz (210–240 g) spinach, coarse stalks removed, washed and drained
1 tbs cornflour
¼ pint (150 ml) skimmed milk plus 2 tbs
½ tsp Dijon mustard
1½ oz (45 g) cheese, grated
1 large egg
1 tbs double cream
freshly grated nutmeg
salt and pepper

SELECTIONS PER SERVING:

½ Milk
2½ Protein
1¼ Vegetable
70 Optional Calories

CALORIES PER
SERVING: 430

SERVES 1
PREPARATION AND COOKING TIME: 25 MINUTES

Put the spinach in a saucepan without any additional liquid, cover and cook over a moderate heat for about 10 minutes or until tender.

Blend the cornflour together with a little milk. Place 2 tablespoons milk into a cup and set aside. Pour the remaining milk into a small saucepan and heat until simmering. Pour the hot milk on to the blended cornflour then return to the heat and boil for 1–2 minutes, stirring all the time. Stir in the mustard and about three-quarters of the cheese.

While the sauce is cooking lightly poach the egg until the white is just set.

Drain the spinach and chop roughly. Blend the cream with the reserved 2 tablespoons of milk then stir into the spinach and season with freshly grated nutmeg, salt and pepper.

Spoon the spinach into a flameproof dish. Make a slight dip in the centre and slide the egg into it. Pour on the cheese sauce then top with the remaining cheese. Cook under a hot grill until bubbling and beginning to brown.

Tip:

If the spinach has very coarse stems buy about 12–14 oz (360–420 g), a lot of weight is lost during preparation.

½ tbs oil
1 small onion, finely chopped
1 small carrot, thinly sliced
1 courgette, sliced
3 button mushrooms, sliced
3 oz (90 g) drained canned
  sweetcorn kernels
1 tbs tomato purée
4 fl oz (120 ml) water or
  vegetable stock
½ tsp dried basil
3 oz (90 g) Quorn

SELECTIONS PER SERVING:

1 Bread
1½ Fat
1½ Protein
2½ Vegetable

CALORIES PER
SERVING: 270

Herby Quorn with Vegetables

SERVES I
PREPARATION AND COOKING TIME: 30 MINUTES

Heat the oil in a small frying pan and cook the onion gently until transparent. Add the other vegetables and the sweetcorn.

Blend the tomato purée with the water or stock, add to the saucepan with the basil and Quorn.

Bring to the boil, stir once, then cover the pan and leave to cook on a low to moderate heat for about 15 minutes or until the vegetables are just cooked.

Variation:

For a more substantial meal, add 3 oz (90 g) canned beans to the Quorn and vegetables, then cook as before. Add 1 Protein Selection and increase Calories per serving to 340.

Right: Herby Quorn with Vegetables

---

6 oz (180 g) potato
1½ tbs chopped fresh chives
2 tsps sunflower seeds
salt and pepper
2 tsps oil

SELECTIONS PER SERVING:

1½ Bread
2 Fat
40 Optional Calories

CALORIES PER
SERVING: 270

Potato Rosti with Chives

SERVES I
PREPARATION AND COOKING TIME: 35 MINUTES

Boil the potato for 10 minutes so that it is slightly cooked but still firm in the middle. Drain and pat dry.

Grate the potato coarsely into a bowl, add the chives, seeds and seasoning and mix well.

Heat the oil in a small frying pan. Divide the mixture into several small mounds and slide into the pan, flattening each with the back of a spoon. Cook over a low heat, turning once, for 15–18 minutes or until golden.

Variation:

Add 1 oz (30 g) finely grated hard cheese to the potato, mix thoroughly and proceed as before. Add 1 Protein Selection and increase Calories per serving to 370.

Spinach and Ham Lasagne

1½ oz (45 g) lasagne (2 sheets)
salt
½ oz (15 g) cornflour
7 fl oz (210 ml) skimmed milk
2 tsps tomato purée
garlic purée
6 oz (180 g) frozen leaf spinach,
   cooked, drained and roughly
   chopped
2 spring onions, chopped
1 oz (30 g) smoked ham, finely
   chopped
pepper
1 oz (30 g) well-flavoured
   cheese, finely grated
¼ tsp Dijon mustard
nutmeg

SELECTIONS PER SERVING:

2 Bread
½ Milk
2 Protein
2 Vegetable
20 Optional Calories

CALORIES PER
SERVING: 510

SERVES I

PREPARATION AND COOKING TIME: 50 MINUTES

Pre-heat the oven to 190°C, 375°F, Gas Mark 5.

Boil the lasagne in lightly salted water for 5–6 minutes. Drain and place on a wire rack to prevent the sheets sticking together.

Blend the cornflour together with the milk. Bring to the boil in a small saucepan, stirring all the time, boil for 2 minutes then remove from the heat.

Blend the tomato purée and a little garlic purée (about ⅛ tsp) with 2 tablespoons of the white sauce and stir into the spinach. Add the spring onion and the ham then season to taste with salt and pepper.

Reserve about 1 tablespoon cheese and add the remainder to the white sauce. Stir in the mustard and season with a little freshly grated nutmeg, salt and pepper.

Spoon about 2 tablespoons of the cheese sauce over the base of a small rectangular dish or pie dish. Lay one sheet of lasagne on top – if you use a pie dish fold the edges over so the lasagne lies flat. Spread the spinach mixture evenly over and lay the second sheet of pasta on top. Spoon the remaining cheese sauce over the lasagne and sprinkle with the cheese. Bake in the pre-heated oven for 25 minutes until bubbling. Brown under a grill if desired.

Variation:

Substitute the smoked ham with 1 oz (30 g) grated or finely diced smoked tofu, reduce the Protein Selections to 1½ and the Total Calories to 485 per serving.

Creamy Leek Tagliatelle

1 tsp margarine
4 oz (120 g) leeks, thinly sliced
2 oz (60 g) tagliatelle
salt
6 tbs skimmed milk
1 tbs double cream
2 oz (60 g) curd cheese
pepper sauce

SELECTIONS PER SERVING:

2 Bread
1 Fat
1 Protein
1¼ Vegetable
60 Optional Calories

CALORIES PER
SERVING: 450

SERVES 1

PREPARATION AND COOKING TIME: 15 MINUTES

Heat the margarine in a small saucepan and stir-fry the leeks for 1–2 minutes then cover the saucepan and cook over a low heat for 6–7 minutes or until just cooked.

Cook the tagliatelle in boiling salted water according to the packaging instructions.

Pour the milk into the leeks and bring to the boil. Add the tagliatelle, stir round and remove from the heat.

Blend the double cream together with the curd cheese and season with a little pepper sauce, add to the tagliatelle and stir until melted.

Variation:

For a more substantial meal stir one lightly beaten egg into the curd cheese and cream, add to the hot leeks and stir round until the egg has cooked sufficiently to thicken the sauce. Add 1 Protein Selection and increase Total Calories per serving to 530.

Chinese Prawn Salad

1½ tsps sherry
¼ tsp light soy sauce
¼ tsp caster sugar
½ tsp wine or sherry vinegar
2 oz (60 g) peeled prawns
2 Chinese leaves, finely
  shredded
½ tsp chopped fresh chives

SELECTIONS PER SERVING:

1 Protein
15 Optional Calories

CALORIES PER
SERVING: 75

SERVES 1

PREPARATION: 5 MINUTES

NO COOKING REQUIRED

Place the sherry, soy sauce, sugar and vinegar in a small bowl and whisk together. Add the prawns and set aside.

Arrange the Chinese leaves on a small serving plate or dish. Spoon on the prawns and dressing and sprinkle with the chives.

Tip:

If time allows leave the prawns to marinate in the dressing for about 1 hour.

Prawn and Broad Bean Salad

1 egg yolk (see Tip below)
2 oz (60 g) peeled prawns
1½ oz (45 g) courgette, diced
2 oz (60 g) broad beans, cooked
1 tbs low fat natural yogurt
1 tbs soured cream
lemon juice
salt and pepper
few colourful salad leaves, e.g.
    radicchio, Lollo roso, Lambs'
    lettuce
2 × ¾ oz (20 g) slices of French
    bread
1 tbs very low fat spread
1 lemon wedge as garnish

SELECTIONS PER SERVING:

2 Bread
1 Fat
1 Protein
¾ Vegetable
90 Optional Calories

CALORIES PER
SERVING: 370

SERVES 1
PREPARATION AND COOKING TIME: 18 MINUTES

Drop the egg yolk into a saucepan of boiling water and cook for 5 minutes or until hard-boiled. To check it is sufficiently cooked gently pierce with the tip of a knife. Leave to cool for a few minutes.

Place the prawns in a bowl, add the courgette. Holding each broad bean between your finger and thumb, squeeze gently so the bean pops out of its waxy skin. Add the beans to the prawns and courgette.

Stir the yogurt together with the soured cream, add a little lemon juice, salt and pepper and stir into the prawns and vegetables. Add the chopped egg yolk.

Arrange the salad leaves on a serving plate or in a bowl, spoon in the salad. Spread the bread with the very low fat spread and arrange on the side of the plate. Serve garnished with a lemon wedge.

Tip:

Cover the egg white and store overnight in the refrigerator for use in another recipe such as Apricot and Orange Snow (see page 70).

Spanish Risotto

1 tsp olive oil
1½ oz (45 g) onion, finely
    chopped
½ clove garlic, finely chopped
1½ oz (45 g) red pepper, finely
    chopped
1 oz (30 g) celery, thinly sliced
1½ oz (45 g) mushrooms,
    chopped
1½ oz (45 g) brown basmati
    rice, well rinsed
scant 4 fl oz (120 ml) vegetable
    or chicken stock
½ tbs tomato purée
good pinch of dried basil

SERVES 1
PREPARATION AND COOKING TIME: 40 MINUTES

Heat the oil in a small saucepan, add the onion and garlic and stir-fry for 1 minute. Add all the remaining vegetables to the saucepan, cover and cook over a low heat for 3 minutes. Stir in the rice, then the stock blended with the tomato purée and the basil. Add the turkey or chicken and ham, and bring the risotto to the boil, stir once then cover the saucepan and leave over a low heat for 25 minutes until cooked.

1 oz (30 g) cooked smoked turkey or chicken, finely chopped
1 oz (30 g) cooked smoked ham, finely chopped

SELECTIONS PER SERVING:

1½ Bread
1 Fat
2 Protein
2 Vegetable

CALORIES PER
SERVING: 325

Variation:

For a vegetarian option omit the smoked meats and substitute 3 oz (90 g) cooked green lentils or cooked kidney beans. The Protein Selections would then be 1. (Total Calories per serving 295.)

---

6 oz (180 g) smoked haddock fillet
¼ pint (150 ml) skimmed milk
1½ tsps margarine
1 small onion, chopped
½ red pepper, deseeded and cut into ½ inch (1.25 cm) squares
1 small courgette, roughly chopped
1 tbs cornflour
1 tbs grated Parmesan cheese

SELECTIONS PER SERVING:

1½ Fat
½ Milk
2½ Protein
2 Vegetable
60 Optional Calories

CALORIES PER
SERVING: 350

Smoked Haddock Gratinée

SERVES 1

PREPARATION AND COOKING TIME: 35 MINUTES

Place the smoked haddock and milk in a saucepan, cover and simmer over a low heat for 7–8 minutes or until the fish is cooked. Using a fish slice, transfer the haddock to a plate, reserving the liquid, remove the skin and separate the fish into large flakes.

Melt the margarine in a saucepan and stir-fry the onion for 2–3 minutes. Add the pepper and stir-fry for a further 3 minutes then mix in the courgette and continue stirring over a moderate heat for 1–2 minutes.

Gradually blend the fish-cooking liquid into the cornflour then pour on to the vegetables. Bring to the boil, stirring all the time, add the flaked haddock and continue to cook for 1 minute, stirring continuously. Add about half the cheese and stir until melted.

Spoon the mixture into a small gratin or flameproof dish, sprinkle with the remaining cheese and cook about 3 inch (7.5 cm) away from a moderate grill for 4 minutes or until bubbling.

Tip:

For a crisp topping sprinkle ½ oz (15 g) fresh breadcrumbs over the dish before grilling, add ½ Bread Selection to your meal and 35 Calories to the total.

1½ tsps margarine
1 oz (30 g) onion, finely
    chopped plus 2 or 3 onion
    rings
6 oz (180 g) sole fillets with
    black skin removed
lemon juice
2–3 tsps finely chopped fresh
    parsley
½ oz (15 g) cornflour
¼ pint (150 ml) skimmed milk
1 oz (30 g) small button
    mushrooms, sliced
salt and pepper

SELECTIONS PER SERVING:

½ Bread
1½ Fat
½ Milk
2½ Protein
¾ Vegetable

CALORIES PER
SERVING: 310

Sole Fillets with Creamy Mushroom Sauce

SERVES I

PREPARATION AND COOKING TIME: 25 MINUTES

Lay a piece of foil, shiny side uppermost, over the base of a grill pan. The foil must be large enough to hold the sole fillets. Grease the foil with a little margarine – no more than ½ teaspoon.

Heat the remaining margarine in a small saucepan, add the chopped onion and cook for 1 minute, then cover the saucepan and steam for 5 minutes over a very low heat.

Place the fillets of fish on the foil, arrange the onion rings on top, add a little lemon juice and sprinkle with the parsley. Draw the foil over and pleat to encase the fish. Place the grill pan about 4 inch (10 cm) away from the heat and cook for about 8 minutes or until the fish is cooked.

Blend the cornflour together with the milk and set aside.

Stir the mushrooms into the onion, cover and leave for 2 minutes then remove the lid and cook over a high heat until the liquid evaporates. Stir in the cornflour and milk and bring to the boil, stirring all the time. Boil for 2–3 minutes, stirring continuously, until thick.

Remove the fish from the heat. Tip the juices out of the foil and into the sauce, season to taste and stir well. Cook over a high heat for 1 minute then pour the sauce on to a warm serving plate and lay the sole on top.

2 spring onions, chopped
1 oz (30 g) fennel, grated
1 small courgette, chopped
4 oz (120 g) skinned cod fillet
¼ pint (150 ml) skimmed milk
½ tbs chopped fresh parsley
salt and pepper
1 tbs cornflour
1 oz (30 g) peeled prawns
lemon juice
1 oz (30 g) fresh breadcrumbs
½ oz (15 g) cheese, grated

Crispy Seafood Crumble

SERVES I

PREPARATION AND COOKING TIME: 30 MINUTES

Place the vegetables and cod in a saucepan. Reserve 2–3 tablespoons milk and pour the remainder over the fish. Add the parsley and season with salt and pepper. Cover the saucepan and cook over a low heat for 9–10 minutes.

Blend the remaining milk with the cornflour. Remove the cod from the saucepan then stir in the blended cornflour and bring to the boil, stirring

SELECTIONS PER SERVING:

1 Bread
½ Milk
2½ Protein
1¼ Vegetable
30 Optional Calories

CALORIES PER
SERVING: 340

all the time. Boil for 1–2 minutes.

Flake the cod into four or five pieces and return to the saucepan with the prawns, stir over a low heat for 1 minute then add lemon juice and salt and pepper to taste.

Spoon the fish and vegetable sauce into a flameproof dish, sprinkle over the breadcrumbs and the cheese. Cook under a hot grill for 2–3 minutes.

Tip:

Serve with brightly coloured vegetables such as green beans and carrots.

½ tbs oil
1 leek, thinly sliced
2 tomatoes, skinned and roughly chopped
3 inch (7.5 cm) wedge of marrow, peeled, deseeded and cut into 1½ inch (4 cm) chunks
1 tsp tomato purée
2 tsps water
salt and pepper
6 oz (180 g) skinned haddock, red mullet, cod or monkfish fillet
6 capers, chopped
2½ tbs low fat natural yogurt

SELECTIONS PER SERVING:

1½ Fat
¼ Milk
2½ Protein
4 Vegetable

CALORIES PER
SERVING: 240

Fish in Leek and Tomato Sauce

SERVES 1

PREPARATION AND COOKING TIME: 50 MINUTES

Pre-heat the oven to 190°C, 375°F, Gas Mark 5.

Heat the oil in a small saucepan and cook the leek gently for 2 minutes. Add the tomatoes and marrow. Blend the tomato purée with the water and stir into the vegetables. Cover the saucepan and leave to cook for 7–8 minutes. Uncover the saucepan, increase the heat and boil fiercely for 1–2 minutes. Season well with salt and pepper.

Spoon the vegetable mixture into a small individual pie dish and lay the fish on top.

Mix the capers with the yogurt then spoon over the fish. Cover with foil and bake in the pre-heated oven for 30 minutes.

Tip:

Serve this dish with a 4 oz (120 g) baked jacket potato which can be cooked at the same time as the fish, and add 1 Bread Selection to the meal, giving a total of 310 Calories per serving.

Curried Chicken and Fruity Rice

½ tbs margarine
1 clove garlic, finely chopped
1 oz (30 g) onion, finely
    chopped
1½ oz (45 g) mixture of red and
    yellow pepper, deseeded and
    finely chopped
3½ oz (105 g) boned skinned
    chicken, cut into 1 inch
    (2.5 cm) cubes
1 oz (30 g) mixture of dried
    chopped apricots and raisins
2 oz (60 g) long grain rice
good pinch of curry powder
6–7 tbs stock
¼ oz (10 g) flaked almonds

SELECTIONS PER SERVING:

2 Bread
1½ Fat
1 Fruit
3 Protein
¾ Vegetable
10 Optional Calories

CALORIES PER
SERVING: 485

SERVES I
PREPARATION AND COOKING TIME: 35 MINUTES

Heat the margarine in a small saucepan, add the garlic, onion and red and yellow pepper and stir round then cover the saucepan, reduce the heat as low as possible and steam for 4 minutes.

Add the chicken and cook briskly over a high heat so it loses its pink colour. Add the apricots and raisins, rice and curry powder then stir in the stock. Bring to the boil, reduce the heat, cover and leave to simmer gently for 20 minutes.

While the chicken and rice are cooking, brown the flaked almonds under a low grill until golden.

Serve the chicken, rice and vegetables on a warm plate with the toasted flaked almonds scattered over.

Variation:

If preferred, lean pork tenderloin may be used in place of the chicken but remember to cook it under a grill, turning once, until the fat stops dripping, then cut it into cubes and mix together with the curry powder and stock.

Left: Curried Chicken and Fruity Rice

Spicy Chicken Curry

2 tsps oil
1 small clove garlic, finely
   chopped
1 small onion, finely chopped
pinch of ground ginger
¼ tsp turmeric
½ tsp chilli powder
¼ tsp ground coriander
¼ tsp ground cumin
3½ oz (105 g) boned skinned
   chicken, cut into ½ inch
   (1.25 cm) cubes
½ tbs flour
1 oz (30 g) mushrooms, sliced
¼–½ red or green pepper,
   deseeded and cut into thin
   1 inch (2.5 cm) lengths
2 oz (60 g) frozen peas
1 oz (30 g) frozen sweetcorn
   kernels
½ oz (15 g) sultanas
¼ pint (150 ml) stock
½ medium banana, sliced
lemon juice
1 tbs low fat natural yogurt

SELECTIONS PER SERVING:

½ Bread
2 Fat
1½ Fruit
2½ Protein
1½ Vegetable
50 Optional Calories

CALORIES PER
SERVING: 380

SERVES I

PREPARATION AND COOKING TIME: I HOUR

Pre-heat the oven to 180°C, 350°F, Gas Mark 4.

Heat the oil in a small flameproof dish, add the garlic and onion and stir-fry for 1–2 minutes. Add the spices and chicken, stir over a moderate heat for 2 minutes. Sprinkle in the flour, stir thoroughly then add all the remaining vegetables and sultanas. Add the stock and bring to the boil, stirring all the time.

Boil for 1 minute then cover the dish and transfer to the pre-heated oven and cook for 25 minutes.

Add the banana to the Spicy Chicken Curry, re-cover and return to the oven to cook for a further 5–10 minutes. Adjust the seasoning, adding lemon juice to taste. Blend in the yogurt and serve.

Variation:

This curry may be cooked on the hob; use a very low heat and stir occasionally to prevent it sticking to the base of the pan.

Stir-fry Chicken in Sherry Sauce

½ tbs oil
½ small onion, finely chopped
1 small clove garlic, finely
    chopped
3½ oz (105 g) boned skinned
    chicken, cut into thin strips
    about 1½ inch (4 cm) long
1 tbs flour
1½ tbs sherry
4 fl oz (120 ml) chicken stock
¼ tsp dried tarragon
1½ oz (45 g) baby button
    mushrooms, halved
¼ red pepper, deseeded and cut
    into thin strips 1 × ¼ inch
    (2.5 cm × 5 mm)
1½ oz (45 g) drained canned
    sweetcorn
salt and pepper

SELECTIONS PER SERVING:

½ Bread
1½ Fat
2½ Protein
1½ Vegetable
55 Optional Calories

CALORIES PER
SERVING: 290

SERVES I

PREPARATION AND COOKING TIME: 45 MINUTES

Heat the oil in a small saucepan or wok and stir-fry the onion and garlic for 2–3 minutes. Add the chicken and stir-fry for 1–2 minutes or until it has almost lost its pinkness.

Sprinkle the flour into the saucepan, gradually blend in the sherry and stock. Add the tarragon, mushrooms, red pepper and sweetcorn. Bring to the boil, stir well, then cover the saucepan and cook over a low heat for 20 minutes, stirring occasionally to prevent sticking. Season to taste with salt and pepper.

Tip:

Serve this dish with 3 oz (90 g) cooked noodles or rice and 6 oz (180 g) crisp mixed salad, but remember to add 1 extra Bread Selection, 2 Vegetable Selections and increase Total Calories per serving to 175.

½ tbs oil
½ onion, finely chopped
2 oz (60 g) parsnip, cut into
 1 × ½ inch (2.5 × 1.25 cm)
 lengths
2 tomatoes, roughly chopped
1 × 1¼ oz (40 g) frankfurter,
 cut into ½ inch (1.25 cm)
 slices
¼ tsp dried oregano
1½ oz (45 g) courgette, cut into
 1 × ½ inch (2.5 × 1.25 cm)
 lengths
2 oz (60 g) frozen peas
salt and pepper
1 oz (30 g) Mozzarella cheese,
 grated

SELECTIONS PER SERVING:

1 Bread
1½ Fat
2 Protein
3 Vegetable

CALORIES PER
SERVING: 340

Frankfurter au Gratin

SERVES 1

PREPARATION AND COOKING TIME: 20 MINUTES

Heat the oil in a saucepan, stir-fry the onion for 1–2 minutes then reduce the heat. Cover the saucepan and leave to steam for 4–5 minutes. Add the parsnip, tomatoes, frankfurter and oregano, cover the saucepan and cook for a further 5–6 minutes.

Add the courgette and frozen peas to the saucepan and bring to the boil, stir thoroughly and season with a little salt and pepper. Reduce the heat, cover the saucepan and leave to simmer for 5 minutes. Be careful not to overcook the vegetables.

Spoon the frankfurter and vegetables into a shallow flameproof dish, sprinkle over the cheese and grill until the cheese has melted and is bubbling.

Variation:

For vegetarians use 3 oz (90 g) diced tofu in place of the frankfurter and reduce Total Calories per serving to 315.

3½ oz (105 g) lean lamb
7 fl oz (210 ml) vegetable or
 chicken stock
½ oz (15 g) green lentils
1 stick celery, cut into chunks
 about 1 inch (2.5 cm)
2 oz (60 g) carrot, cut into
 chunks about 1 inch (2.5 cm)
2 oz (60 g) onion, cut into
 chunks about 1 inch (2.5 cm)
4 oz (120 g) potato, cut into
 chunks about 1 inch (2.5 cm)
1 oz (30 g) drained canned or
 frozen sweetcorn kernels
2 oz (60 g) frozen chopped
 spinach

Lamb and Lentil Stew

SERVES 1

PREPARATION AND COOKING TIME: 50 MINUTES

Cut the lamb into five or six pieces, place in a small saucepan and cover with the stock. Bring slowly to boiling point, reduce the heat and simmer for 3–4 minutes then leave to cool.

Place the lentils in a small saucepan, cover with water and bring to the boil. Boil for 10 minutes.

Skim off all the fat that solidifies on top of the lamb. Remove the lamb from the stock and place in a saucepan with the prepared vegetables, sweetcorn and spinach. Pour the stock into a measuring jug.

½ tbs tomato purée
¼ tsp mixed dried herbs

SELECTIONS PER SERVING:

1½ Bread
3 Protein
2½ Vegetable
25 Optional Calories

CALORIES PER
SERVING: 375

Remove the lentils from their cooking liquid and add to the lamb and vegetables. If necessary pour some of their cooking liquid into the measuring jug to make the stock up to 7 fl oz (210 ml).

Blend the stock with the tomato purée, add the herbs and stir into the lamb and vegetables. Bring to the boil over a moderate heat, stir well, cover and cook on a very low heat for 35 minutes. Stir once or twice during the cooking time.

Tip:

If you find it difficult to control the hob heat, buy a simmering gauze from a kitchen or hardware shop. The mesh spreads the heat evenly over the base of the saucepan.

1 medium orange
1½ tsps margarine
1 small onion, chopped
4 oz (120 g) lamb's liver, cut
   into thin strips
1 tsp chopped fresh parsley to
   garnish

SELECTIONS PER SERVING:

1½ Fat
1 Fruit
3 Protein
½ Vegetable

CALORIES PER
SERVING: 325

Liver and Orange Stir-fry

SERVES 1

PREPARATION AND COOKING TIME: 20 MINUTES

Cut the orange in half lengthways. Cut the zest and pith from one half and divide it into segments, removing as much of the membrane as possible. Squeeze the juice from the other half.

Heat the margarine in a frying pan and stir-fry the onion for 2 minutes. Add the liver and stir-fry for 3–4 minutes.

Pour the orange juice into the pan, stir well and simmer for 3–4 minutes over a low heat. Add the orange segments and heat through gently.

Spoon the liver and orange into a serving bowl or on to a plate and sprinkle with parsley.

Tip:

Before you start to cook this recipe put 2 oz (60 g) rice or pasta into a saucepan, bring to the boil and cook while preparing the liver. Add 2 Bread Selections to your meal. Calories per serving will then become 485.

Minced Beef and Haricot Bean Pie

3 oz (90 g) minced beef
½ onion, finely chopped
1 carrot, finely chopped
1 stick celery, finely chopped
4 fl oz (120 ml) beef stock
4 oz (120 g) potato, whole
salt
3 oz (90 g) canned baked beans
pepper sauce
1 tsp margarine

SELECTIONS PER SERVING:

2 Bread
1 Fat
2½ Protein
1½ Vegetable

CALORIES PER
SERVING: 360

SERVES I

PREPARATION AND COOKING TIME: 50 MINUTES

Place the minced beef in a small saucepan and add the onion, carrot and celery, stir in the beef stock. Bring to the boil, cover and simmer for 25 minutes. Remove from the heat and leave until cool then skim the fat off the top.

Cook the whole potato in lightly salted water for about 15 minutes or until just cooked, remove from the water and cool under running cold water.

Stir the baked beans into the minced beef mixture, bring to the boil over a moderate heat and boil for a few minutes to reduce the liquid. Season with salt and a little pepper sauce and spoon into a small flameproof dish about 5 inch (12.5 cm) in diameter.

Thinly slice the potato and arrange the slices overlapping on top of the beef. Dot the margarine over the potato slices and cook under a hot grill until golden brown.

Tip:

The baked beans in tomato sauce are added after the minced beef has been cooked and the fat removed because their sauce would absorb some of the fat.

Illustrated on
pages 58/59

Toad in the Hole

1½ oz (45 g) plain flour
1 egg
4 tbs skimmed milk
salt and pepper
1 × 2 oz (60 g) pork and beef
  sausage
½ tbs oil

SELECTIONS PER SERVING:

1½ Bread
1½ Fat
2½ Protein
20 Optional Calories

SERVES I

PREPARATION AND COOKING TIME: 45 MINUTES

Pre-heat the oven to 220°C, 425°F, Gas Mark 7.

Sieve the flour into a bowl, make a well in the centre and break the egg into it. Add 1 tablespoon milk and, using a fork or wooden spoon, mix until smooth. Gradually blend in the remaining milk and season with salt and pepper.

Cook the sausage under a moderate grill for about 12 minutes until cooked.

CALORIES PER
SERVING: 435

Spoon the oil into a shallow 5½–6 inch (14–15 cm) metal dish – a small sandwich tin would be suitable. Place the tin in the pre-heated oven for 3–4 minutes.

Slice the cooked sausage and arrange the slices in the hot oil, return the tin to the oven for a further 3 minutes until the fat is very hot and beginning to smoke.

Stir the batter and pour into the tin. Return to the oven and cook for 15–20 minutes until well risen, puffy and golden brown.

Variation:

Use a frankfurter sausage in place of the pork and beef sausage and sprinkle with a little Parmesan cheese before serving. Remember to adjust the Optional Calories as necessary.

---

3 medium dried prunes
1 oz (30 g) dried apricots
grated zest and juice of ½ a lemon
2 tsps honey
large pinch of ground allspice
2 tbs frozen whipped topping

SELECTIONS PER SERVING:

2 Fruit
70 Optional Calories

CALORIES PER
SERVING: 180

Prune and Apricot Compôte

SERVES 1
PREPARATION AND COOKING TIME: 15 MINUTES PLUS SOAKING TIME

Cover the prunes and apricots with cold water and leave for several hours or overnight. Cover the lemon zest with clingfilm and put in the refrigerator.

Place the fruit in a small saucepan and add 4 tablespoons of water, including the liquid the fruit has been soaking in. Add the lemon juice, honey and allspice; place over a moderate heat and simmer for 10–12 minutes.

Spoon the compôte into a serving dish and serve hot, warm or chilled. Before serving top with the frozen whipped topping and sprinkle with the reserved lemon zest.

Variation:

This compôte may be served for breakfast; substitute the frozen whipped topping with 2½ fl oz (75 ml) low fat natural yogurt, add ½ Milk Selection and reduce the Optional Calories to 40.

Creamy Nectarine

1 medium nectarine or peach,
  stoned and roughly chopped
2 tsps sherry
2½ tbs low fat natural yogurt
1 tbs thick single or double
  cream
¼ tsp caster sugar
⅛ tsp ground cinnamon

SELECTIONS PER SERVING:

1 Fruit
¼ Milk
45 Optional Calories

CALORIES PER
SERVING: 140

SERVES I

PREPARATION: 5 MINUTES PLUS MARINATING TIME

NO COOKING REQUIRED

Place the nectarine or peach in a non-metallic bowl and sprinkle with the sherry. Leave to marinate for 30 minutes or more, stirring once or twice.

Gently blend the yogurt with the cream, just enough to mix, do not over-stir or the cream will become runny.

Spoon the nectarine and sherry into a serving glass and cover with the cream and yogurt.

Mix the caster sugar and cinnamon together and sprinkle over the cream and yogurt just before serving.

Tip:

The extra thick creams are ideal for small quantities of mixture when there is not sufficient cream to whip. Use the minimum amount of stirring, as the texture breaks down and the cream will become runny.

Papaya Delight

½ medium papaya, deseeded
1 tsp lime juice
1 tsp caster sugar
1½ tbs single cream
slice of lime to garnish

SELECTIONS PER SERVING:

1 Fruit
65 Optional Calories

CALORIES PER
SERVING: 115

SERVES I

PREPARATION: 10 MINUTES

NO COOKING REQUIRED

Remove the flesh from the papaya and process in a liquidiser with the lime juice, caster sugar and cream until smooth.

Transfer the creamed papaya to a serving glass and chill until required. Serve with a slice of lime.

Tip:

If you don't own a liquidiser press the papaya through a sieve then stir in the lime juice, sugar and cream.

Summer Cup

For the salad:
½ medium Charentais melon, deseeded
2 oz (60 g) cherries, stoned
2 oz (60 g) raspberries
½ tsp caster sugar
For the topping:
2 tbs low fat natural yogurt
1 tsp caster sugar

SELECTIONS PER SERVING:

2 Fruit
50 Optional Calories

CALORIES PER
SERVING: 130

SERVES 1
PREPARATION: 10 MINUTES
NO COOKING REQUIRED

Using a teaspoon or melon baller, carefully remove as much flesh as possible from the melon and place in a bowl with any juice which escapes during preparation. Add the cherries, raspberries and the ½ tsp caster sugar, mix well. Spoon the fruit into the melon skin and chill until required.

Mix the yogurt and 1 tsp caster sugar together. Just before serving, pour the sweetened yogurt over the fruit.

Tip:

Choose a really ripe melon, if you prefer substitute half a Rock or Ogen melon. To test a melon for ripeness press very gently, if it is ripe the skin should 'give' a little and the fruit smell sweet.

Right: Summer Cup

Apricot and Orange Snow

6 oz (180 g) drained canned
   apricots
½ tbs frozen concentrated
   orange juice, thawed
ground ginger or cinnamon
½ tsp caster sugar
1 egg white
pinch of cream of tartar

SELECTIONS PER SERVING:

1½ Fruit
45 Optional Calories

CALORIES PER
SERVING: 120

SERVES 1
PREPARATION: 5 MINUTES
NO COOKING REQUIRED

Mash the apricots with a fork until fairly smooth – if you have a small liquidiser they may be puréed. Blend in the orange juice, a good pinch of ground ginger or cinnamon and the caster sugar.

Not more than 20 minutes before serving whisk the egg white together with the cream of tartar until peaking. Fold into the fruit purée, spoon into a serving glass and sprinkle with a little more spice.

Variation:

To make Mango and Orange Snow omit the apricots and add the flesh of one medium mango. The Fruit Selection would then be increased to 2 and the Total Calories per serving to 145.

Peach and Grapefruit Flummery

1 medium peach, stoned and
   roughly chopped
juice of ½ medium grapefruit
2 tsps arrowroot or cornflour
1 tsp sugar
1 tbs soured cream
½ tsp desiccated or shredded
   coconut, toasted

SELECTIONS PER SERVING:

2 Fruit
75 Optional Calories

CALORIES PER
SERVING: 150

SERVES 1
PREPARATION AND COOKING TIME: 14 MINUTES PLUS CHILLING

Place the peach and grapefruit juice in a liquidiser and process to a purée. Sieve the purée to remove any skin and membrane.

Blend the arrowroot or cornflour to a smooth paste with a little of the fruit purée then stir in the rest of the purée and the sugar. Pour into a small saucepan and bring to the boil, boil for 1–2 minutes, stirring all the time.

Leave to cool for 1–2 minutes then pour the fruit into a wine glass or narrow dessert glass, leave to cool then chill until ready to serve.

Spread the soured cream over the flummery then sprinkle the toasted coconut on top.

Variation:

This recipe can easily be altered to serve two, three or more people, just multiply the ingredients by the number to be served.

Gooseberry and Vanilla Fool

5 oz (150 g) gooseberries,
   topped and tailed
1½ tbs water
small sprig of elderflowers
   (optional)
2½ tsps custard powder
¼ pint (150 ml) skimmed milk
artificial sweetener
¼–½ tsp lemon juice
few drops of green colouring
   (optional)
5 fl oz (150 ml) very low fat
   vanilla yogurt

SELECTIONS PER SERVING:

1 Fruit
½ Milk
140 Optional Calories

CALORIES PER
SERVING: 195

SERVES 1

PREPARATION AND COOKING TIME: 15 MINUTES PLUS CHILLING

Place the gooseberries in a small saucepan, add the water and elderflowers, cover and cook gently over a low heat for about 10 minutes or until the berries are soft.

Blend the custard powder with 2 tablespoons milk. Heat the remaining milk then stir the blended custard powder into the saucepan and bring to the boil, stirring all the time.

Pour the custard and gooseberries into a liquidiser and process to a purée. Pour the purée back into the saucepan and return to the boil, stirring continuously. Boil for 2 minutes until very thick.

Remove from the heat and sweeten to taste with artificial sweetener and about ¼–½ teaspoon lemon juice. If desired stir a little green colouring into the mixture. Leave until cool.

Stir the vanilla yogurt through the gooseberry mixture and spoon into a serving glass or bowl. Chill until ready to serve.

Tip:

This recipe makes a very generous serving for one. The same quantities could be used to make a light dessert to serve two people after a rich main course; remember to halve the Selections and Optional Calories.

Illustrated on page 62

Cold Creations

Cold Creations offers a variety of sweet and savoury dishes which are served chilled or cold. They are suitable for many occasions, from tea-time treats to starters, main courses or desserts.

Salads are an obvious choice for healthy eating and can be prepared in advance and left ready-to-eat, loosely covered in the refrigerator. They don't have to just consist of a lettuce leaf and sliced tomato but can include a variety of delicious ingredients. What makes a salad really special is its dressing and there is a wide variety to choose from in Cold Creations, such as yogurt and mint (page 90), blue cheese (page 99) or avocado mayonnaise (page 93). Unless the recipe specifies to coat the salad with a dressing it is better to add it just before serving.

Some of the tea-time or dessert recipes use the fresh fruit that is in season but the majority can be made at any time of the year by using frozen or canned fruits. The sorbets and sherbets have to be a favourite choice and they look extremely good on the dinner table as well as being very refreshing.

The recipes in this section are not created only to be served in summer. They are suitable additions for meals of every season and being so quick and simple to prepare they make the life of the hostess, busy mother or business person very easy.

Cauliflower, Tofu and Apple Salad

7–8 oz (210–240 g) cauliflower florets
4 tsps mayonnaise
3 oz (90 g) silken tofu
1–2 tsps lemon juice
2 tsps chopped fresh dill
salt and pepper
2 oz (60 g) fennel, thinly sliced
1 medium crisp apple, roughly chopped
½ oz (15 g) pecan kernels, roughly chopped

SELECTIONS PER SERVING:

1 Fat
½ Protein
¾ Vegetable
20 Optional Calories

CALORIES PER
SERVING: 70

SERVES 4

PREPARATION AND COOKING TIME: 15 MINUTES

Plunge the cauliflower florets into a saucepan of boiling water, return to the boil and cook for 2–3 minutes, drain and cool under running cold water.

Blend the mayonnaise with the tofu, stir in the lemon juice and dill and season with a little salt and pepper.

Mix the cauliflower, fennel and apple together in a bowl, stir in the creamy dressing to evenly coat the ingredients then transfer to a serving bowl. Scatter over the pecan kernels and serve.

Variation:

You can substitute the pecan kernels with walnuts and add 2 oz (60 g) diced Edam cheese. Add ½ Protein to the Selections and increase the Total Calories per serving to 250.

Beansprout Salad

8 oz (240 g) beansprouts
1 large red pepper, deseeded and finely chopped
2 tbs orange juice
¼ tsp caster sugar
2 tsps soy sauce
1 tsp lemon juice

SELECTIONS PER SERVING:

1 Vegetable
5 Optional Calories

CALORIES PER
SERVING: 15

SERVES 4

PREPARATION: 10 MINUTES

NO COOKING REQUIRED

Mix together the beansprouts and the red pepper in a salad bowl.

Pour the orange juice into a small bowl, add the sugar, soy sauce and lemon juice and whisk together with a fork.

To serve, pour the dressing over the salad and toss well.

Tip:

This recipe looks particularly attractive served in a bowl lined with red chicory or radicchio leaves.

Broad Bean and Soured Cream Ring

**1 lb (480 g) frozen or fresh
    podded broad beans**
1 tbs margarine
1 tbs flour
½ pint (300 ml) skimmed milk
**2 oz (60 g) Parmesan cheese,
    finely grated**
2 eggs, separated
1½–2 tbs lemon juice
salt and pepper
freshly grated nutmeg
6 tbs soured cream
1 red pepper
2 tbs water
4 tsps gelatine

SELECTIONS PER SERVING:

½ Bread
½ Fat
½ Protein
½ Vegetable
75 Optional Calories

CALORIES PER
SERVING: 185

SERVES 6

PREPARATION AND COOKING TIME: 40 MINUTES

PLUS COOLING AND CHILLING

Cook the broad beans until soft, drain and cool under running cold water.

While the beans are cooking melt the margarine in a saucepan, add the flour and stir over a low heat. Gradually blend in the milk and bring to the boil, stirring all the time. Boil for 1–2 minutes. Stir in the cheese then pour the sauce into a liquidiser.

Gently press the beans between your finger and thumb and slip each one out of its waxy skin – this will take 10–15 minutes but the beans can't be pushed through a sieve as the skins completely block the holes, even after liquidising. Add the beans to the liquidiser and process to a purée. Add the egg yolks and process once again. Pour the purée into a clean bowl.

Season the purée with lemon juice and plenty of salt, pepper and freshly grated nutmeg. Stir in the soured cream and set aside until cool then chill in the refrigerator while preparing the rest of the recipe.

Lay the red pepper in a grill pan and cook under a high heat, turning two or three times, until black and charred all over. Cool under running cold water then strip off the skin and dab with kitchen paper. Chop the flesh into small pieces and stir into the broad bean purée.

Pour the water into a cup or small bowl, sprinkle in the gelatine and stir well then stand in a saucepan of simmering water until the gelatine has dissolved. Stir a little of the purée into the gelatine then stir the gelatine mixture into the bowl of purée. Chill until beginning to set.

Whisk the egg whites, together with a pinch of salt, until peaking then gently fold into the setting purée. Spoon the mixture into a mould and leave until completely set. To serve; dip the mould briefly in hot water and invert on to a serving plate.

Tip:

Make this recipe in a ring mould then invert and serve filled with a vegetable or prawn salad. Substitute the gelatine with a vegetable setting agent if you wish to make this for a vegetarian.

Green Salad with Yogurt

For the dressing:
3 tbs low fat natural yogurt
**1½ tbs finely chopped fresh
    mint**
1 tbs olive oil
lemon juice
1 tbs skimmed milk
**1 tbs thick single or double
    cream**
For the salad:
**mixture of salad leaves e.g.
    Chinese leaves, chicory,
    Frisée, Lambs' lettuce, Cos
    lettuce**
1 courgette, thinly sliced
**1 green pepper, deseeded and
    sliced**

SELECTIONS PER SERVING:

½ Fat
1 Vegetable
25 Optional Calories

CALORIES PER
SERVING: 70

SERVES 4

PREPARATION: 10 MINUTES PLUS CHILLING

NO COOKING REQUIRED

In a bowl mix together the yogurt, mint, oil and about ¾ teaspoon lemon juice. Stir in the milk and cream – just enough to mix – do not over-stir or the cream will thin.

Cover the bowl and leave in the refrigerator for 1–2 hours for the mint flavour to develop. Add a little more lemon juice if desired.

Shred or tear the salad leaves into a bowl, add the courgette and green pepper and mix together gently.

To serve; either arrange the salad in four small salad bowls and spoon the dressing in the centre of each salad, or leave the salad in a large bowl and hand the dressing round separately.

Tip:

The dressing can be made the day before it is to be used and stored in the refrigerator. It can be served with a wide variety of vegetable or fruit and vegetable salads.

Avocado and Pear Salad

**1 medium pear, peeled, cored
    and cut into ½ inch
    (1.25 cm) pieces**
**½ medium papaya, peeled,
    deseeded and cut into ½ inch
    (1.25 cm) pieces**
**4 oz (120 g) avocado, peeled,
    stoned and cut into 1 inch
    (2.5 cm) pieces**
3 tbs raspberry vinegar
Frisée

SELECTIONS PER SERVING:

1 Fat
½ Fruit

CALORIES PER
SERVING: 85

SERVES 4

PREPARATION: 10 MINUTES

NO COOKING REQUIRED

Mix all the prepared fruit and avocado in a bowl and stir in the vinegar.

To serve, arrange a few leaves of Frisée on each serving plate and spoon the mixture on top.

Variation:

This recipe can also be served as an appetiser or a side salad.

mixture of salad leaves e.g.
   lettuce, chicory, Frisée
2 oz (60 g) cashew nut kernels,
   roughly chopped
2 oz (60 g) Mycella or
   Gorgonzola cheese
8 radishes, sliced
1 green pepper, halved,
   deseeded and cut into half-
   circle slices
1 red or yellow pepper, halved,
   deseeded and cut into half-
   circle slices
4 oz (120 g) fennel, thinly sliced
2 medium oranges
For the dressing:
2 tsps clear honey
2 tsps olive or hazelnut oil
2 tsps wine vinegar
salt and pepper
pinch of powdered mustard

SELECTIONS PER SERVING:

1 Fat
½ Fruit
1½ Protein
1 Vegetable
10 Optional Calories

CALORIES PER
SERVING: 200

Cashew Nut, Orange and Blue Cheese Salad

SERVES 4
PREPARATION: 15 MINUTES
NO COOKING REQUIRED

Put the salad leaves in a salad bowl, add the cashew nut kernels and crumble in the cheese. Mix in all the prepared vegetables. Prepare the oranges, use a sharp knife to remove the zest and white pith, then cut between the membranes and remove the segments. Catch the juice which runs from the oranges during preparation. Stir the orange segments into the salad.

Make the dressing; pour the reserved orange juice into a screw-top jar together with the honey, oil, vinegar, salt, pepper and mustard. Shake well to mix. Alternatively whisk the ingredients together in a small bowl.

Pour the dressing over the salad, toss well and then serve.

Right: Cashew Nut, Orange and Blue Cheese Salad

Apple and Blue Cheese Potato Salad

2 oz (60 g) blue cheese e.g.
    Stilton or Danish blue;
    crumbled
2 medium crisp apples, diced
4 sticks celery, diced
12 oz (360 g) cooked potatoes,
    diced
2 oz (60 g) cooked ham, diced
2 tbs buttermilk
1 tbs lemon juice
4 tsps mayonnaise
1 tbs chopped fresh dill, plus a
    little extra for garnish
salt and pepper

SELECTIONS PER SERVING:

½ Bread
1 Fat
½ Fruit
1 Protein
½ Vegetable
25 Optional Calories

CALORIES PER
SERVING: 200

SERVES 4

PREPARATION: 10 MINUTES

NO COOKING REQUIRED

Mix the cheese, apples and celery with the potatoes and ham.

Place the buttermilk, lemon juice, mayonnaise and dill in a small bowl, season to taste with salt and pepper and whisk together with a fork. Pour the dressing over the salad and toss well to mix.

To serve; spoon the dressed salad into a bowl and garnish with dill.

Tip:

Use apples which have a good flavour such as Cox's Orange Pippins or Russets.

Seeded Rice Salad

6 oz (180 g) basmati rice
2 tsps sesame seeds
1 clove garlic, crushed
2 tbs tahini
1 tsp wine vinegar
1½ tbs water
salt and pepper
1½ tbs sunflower seeds
1½ tbs pumpkin seeds

SELECTIONS PER SERVING:

1½ Bread
½ Fat
½ Protein
55 Optional Calories

CALORIES PER
SERVING: 245

SERVES 4

PREPARATION AND COOKING TIME: 30 MINUTES

Cook the rice until the grains are just tender and separate (about 15 minutes).

Sprinkle the sesame seeds on a grill pan lined with foil and cook under a moderate grill until golden.

Put the garlic, tahini, vinegar and water in a small bowl and whisk together using a fork until evenly combined. Season to taste with salt and pepper.

Stir the tahini dressing through the warm rice and leave to cool, stirring occasionally to prevent the rice sticking in clumps. Leave until cold.

Stir all the seeds into the rice and serve.

Salad Roulade with Avocado Mayonnaise

1½ oz (45 g) breadcrumbs made
  from 2-day-old bread
2 oz (60 g) Parmesan cheese,
  grated
2 eggs, separated
½ tsp Dijon mustard
4 fl oz (120 ml) skimmed milk
salt
1 tbs mayonnaise
4 oz (120 g) fromage frais
3 oz (90 g) avocado
pepper sauce
finely shredded crisp lettuce
  leaves

SELECTIONS PER SERVING:

1 Fat
1 Protein
25 Optional Calories

CALORIES PER
SERVING: 145

SERVES 6

PREPARATION AND COOKING TIME: 35 MINUTES

Pre-heat the oven to 200°C, 400°F, Gas Mark 6.

Line a 11 × 7 inch (27.5 × 17.5 cm) Swiss-roll tin with non-stick baking parchment.

Mix the breadcrumbs and cheese together in a large bowl.

In a small bowl mix the egg yolks with the mustard and milk then stir into the breadcrumbs and cheese.

Add a pinch of salt to the egg whites and whisk until peaking. Using a metal tablespoon, carefully fold the egg whites into the breadcrumb mixture. Spoon the mixture into the lined tin – place spoonfuls of the mixture all over the tin so only a minimum amount of spreading evenly is required, or the air will be knocked out of the mixture.

Cook in the pre-heated oven for 18–20 minutes until light golden brown and firm to touch. Remove the tin from the oven. Dampen a clean cloth under running cold water then wring out to remove as much of the water as possible. Lay the cloth over the baked roulade and leave until cold.

Shortly before serving blend the mayonnaise with the fromage frais. Mash the avocado and add to the mixture. Season to taste with salt and pepper sauce.

Turn the cold roulade out on to a sheet of non-stick baking parchment. Spread with the avocado mayonnaise then scatter over the lettuce.

Using the paper to support the roulade, roll it up Swiss-roll style. Transfer to a board or plate and serve whole or cut into six slices.

Variation:

To make a more substantial meal, scatter 4 oz (120 g) chopped, peeled prawns over the Avocado Mayonnaise then roll up the roulade. Increase the Optional Calories to 45 and the Total Calories per serving to 165.

Salad Roulade with Avocado Mayonnaise *illustrated overleaf*

Salmon Mousse

1 oz (30 g) margarine
1 oz (30 g) flour
½ pint (300 ml) skimmed milk
9 oz (270 g) well-drained
    canned salmon
1½ tsps tomato ketchup
6 oz (180 g) fromage frais
    (8% fat)
salt and pepper
2 tbs hot water
1 sachet gelatine
2 egg whites
slices of cucumber and thinly
    sliced lemon to garnish
    (optional)

SELECTIONS PER SERVING:

1 Fat
2 Protein
35 Optional Calories

CALORIES PER
SERVING: 160

Salmon Mousse illustrated on previous
page

SERVES 6

PREPARATION AND COOKING TIME: 20 MINUTES PLUS SETTING

Melt the margarine in a saucepan, add the flour and stir well then remove from the heat and gradually blend in the milk. Bring to the boil, stirring all the time, cook for 2 minutes until thick and smooth. Leave to cool then pour into a liquidiser or food processor, add the salmon and tomato ketchup and process until smooth. Add the fromage frais and process once again. Pour into a bowl and season to taste with salt and pepper.

Spoon the water into a cup or small basin, sprinkle in the gelatine, stir well then stand in a saucepan of simmering water until completely dissolved. Stir a little of the salmon mixture into the dissolved gelatine then stir the gelatine into the salmon. Leave until beginning to set.

Whisk the egg whites with a pinch of salt until peaking, gently fold into the setting mousse. Spoon the mixture into one large mould or individual moulds and chill in the refrigerator until completely set. Dip the mousse briefly in hot water then invert on to a serving plate prior to serving. Garnish the mousse with slices of cucumber and lemon.

Tip:

Serve with thin slices of wholemeal or granary bread allowing 1 oz (30 g) per serving, add 1 Bread Selection and increase Total Calories per serving to 230.

Curried Parsnip Salad

2 tsps oil
½ onion, finely chopped
approximately 2 tsps curry
    powder
1 lb (480 g) parsnips, cut into
    1½ × ½ inch (4 × 1.25 cm)
    lengths
2 tbs water
4 oz (120 g) fromage frais
1–2 tsps lemon juice
salt and pepper

SERVES 4

PREPARATION AND COOKING TIME: 15 MINUTES PLUS COOLING

Heat the oil in a saucepan and stir-fry the onion for 1–2 minutes. Stir in the curry powder then add the parsnips and water. Cover the saucepan and cook gently over a low heat for about 8 minutes or until the parsnip is just tender. Remove the saucepan from the heat and leave to cool a little.

Blend the fromage frais with the lemon juice then stir into the curried

SELECTIONS PER SERVING:

1 Bread
½ Fat
½ Protein
¼ Vegetable

CALORIES PER
SERVING: 110

parsnips. Season to taste with salt and pepper and add a little more lemon juice if desired. Refrigerate until ready to serve.

Tip:

Many different root vegetables may be cooked using the quantities given in this recipe. For example, carrot and swede may be used in place of the parsnip but remember to adjust the Selections as necessary.

---

4 oz (120 g) macaroni
salt
3 sticks celery, diagonally sliced
2 oz (60 g) Cheddar cheese,
    coarsely grated
2 oz (60 g) red Leicester cheese,
    coarsely grated
½ small onion, finely grated
10 small stuffed olives, halved or
    sliced
4 tsps mayonnaise
4 tbs low fat natural yogurt
few salad leaves
2 tomatoes, cut into thin wedges
paprika

SELECTIONS PER SERVING:

1 Bread
1 Fat
1 Protein
1 Vegetable
20 Optional Calories

CALORIES PER
SERVING: 250

Macaroni Cheese Salad

SERVES 4

PREPARATION AND COOKING TIME: 20 MINUTES

Cook the macaroni in lightly salted boiling water according to the packaging instructions.

Mix together the celery, cheeses, onion and olives in a large bowl.

Blend the mayonnaise with the yogurt. Drain the macaroni and cool under running cold water. Stir in the mayonnaise and yogurt.

Arrange the salad leaves on four serving plates. Mix the macaroni and mayonnaise mixture with the cheese and vegetables, stir well. Spoon the macaroni salad in the centre of each plate.

To serve, arrange the tomatoes round the macaroni and sprinkle each serving with a little paprika.

Tip:

This salad may be prepared in advance then covered and refrigerated until required.

Tabbouleh

4 oz (120 g) bulgar wheat
8 fl oz (240 ml) boiling water
4 tbs lemon juice
4 tomatoes, skinned and roughly
    chopped
1 small green pepper, deseeded
    and finely chopped
1 small red pepper, deseeded
    and finely chopped
3 oz (90 g) spring onions, thinly
    sliced
2–3 tbs chopped fresh parsley
2 tsps chopped fresh mint
2 tbs olive oil
½ tsp salt
good pinch of ground coriander
good pinch of ground cumin
sprigs of mint and slices of
    lemon to garnish (optional)

SELECTIONS PER SERVING:

1 Bread
1½ Fat
1½ Vegetable

CALORIES PER
SERVING: 180

SERVES 4

PREPARATION: 15 MINUTES PLUS SOAKING
NO COOKING REQUIRED

Place the bulgar wheat in a bowl, pour over the boiling water, stir in the lemon juice and set aside for 30–40 minutes until all the liquid has been absorbed. Mix in the prepared vegetables.

Whisk the herbs, olive oil, salt and spices together in a small bowl, then pour over the salad and stir thoroughly.

To serve, spoon the salad into an attractive bowl and garnish with sprigs of mint and slices of lemon if desired.

Tip One:

To skin the tomatoes cover with boiling water, leave for 30–40 seconds, drain and peel off the skins.

Tip Two:

This salad can be prepared well in advance, covered with clingfilm and stored in the refrigerator.

Illustrated on page 2

Red Cabbage and Pineapple Salad

2 oz (60 g) drained canned
    pineapple, chopped, plus
    4 tbs of juice
3 oz (90 g) redcurrants
6 oz (180 g) red cabbage, finely
    shredded
¼ tsp caraway seeds
½ tsp sugar
2–3 tsps lemon juice

SELECTIONS PER SERVING:

½ Vegetable
20 Optional Calories

CALORIES PER
SERVING: 25

SERVES 4

PREPARATION AND COOKING TIME: 15 MINUTES

Pour the pineapple juice into a small saucepan, add the redcurrants, cover the saucepan and cook gently over a low heat until the juice runs from the currants. Stir in the cabbage, pineapple, caraway seeds, sugar and 2 teaspoons lemon juice and mix well. Return the saucepan to the heat, cover and simmer for 5 minutes.

Remove the lid from the saucepan, increase the heat and boil for 1 minute. Take off the heat and leave to cool. Add a little more lemon juice to taste, spoon into an attractive bowl and serve.

Mixed Salad
with Blue Cheese Dressing

1 small head radicchio, leaves separated and shredded

1 small head chicory, leaves separated and shredded

1 red or yellow pepper, halved, deseeded and cut into half rings

2 sticks celery, chopped

3 spring onions, chopped

2 medium seedless oranges

For the dressing:

4 oz (120 g) blue cheese e.g. Gorgonzola or Danish blue, grated

2 tsps olive oil

5–6 tbs cider or white wine vinegar

pepper

SELECTIONS PER SERVING:

½ Fat
½ Fruit
1 Protein
1¼ Vegetable

CALORIES PER SERVING: 150

SERVES 4
PREPARATION: 15 MINUTES
NO COOKING REQUIRED

Mix together the radicchio, chicory, red or yellow pepper, celery and spring onions. Using a sharp knife cut the peel and pith off the oranges, cut in half lengthways then slice. Mix with the other salad ingredients.

To make the dressing, mash the cheese with a fork in a small bowl then gradually blend in the oil and cider or wine vinegar; season with a little pepper.

Serve the salad and dressing separately. Spoon the dressing over the salad just before eating.

Tip:

The salad ingredients may be adjusted to suit your taste. For example the radicchio and chicory could be replaced by Chinese leaves or Cos lettuce.

Right: Mixed Salad with Blue Cheese Dressing

Sponge-Based Lemon Cheesecake

1 egg (size 2)
2 oz (60 g) caster sugar
1½ oz (45 g) plain flour
½ oz (15 g) cornflour
½ tsp baking powder
8 oz (240 g) cottage cheese
8 oz (240 g) curd cheese
12 fl oz (360 ml) skimmed milk
¼ tsp vanilla essence
1½ tbs lemon juice
artificial sweetener
2 tbs water
2 tbs gelatine
3 egg whites
pinch of cream of tartar

SELECTIONS PER SERVING:

½ Protein
80 Optional Calories

CALORIES PER
SERVING: 125

SERVES 10
PREPARATION AND COOKING TIME: 40 MINUTES
PLUS COOLING AND SETTING

Pre-heat the oven to 180°C, 350°F, Gas Mark 4.

Line the base and sides of a 10 inch (25 cm) loose-bottomed flan tin with non-stick baking parchment.

Break the egg into a bowl, add the caster sugar and place on top of a saucepan of simmering water. Whisk continuously until thick and creamy, when the whisk is lifted from the mixture it leaves a trail.

Sift the flour, cornflour and baking powder together and gently fold into the whisked mixture with 1 tablespoon warm water. Spoon the mixture evenly all over the base of the lined flan tin so hardly any spreading is required. Bake in the pre-heated oven for about 15 minutes or until golden and when lightly pressed the cake feels springy. Leave to cool in the flan tin. When cold turn the sponge out on to a plate and remove the paper base.

Re-line the flan tin and sides, securing the paper so it is about 1½ inch (4 cm) higher than the sides of the tin. Place the sponge in the tin.

Process the cottage and curd cheeses with the milk in a liquidiser or food processor until smooth. Add the vanilla essence and lemon juice and process once again then pour into a bowl. Sweeten to taste with artificial sweetener.

Pour the water into a cup or small bowl, sprinkle in the gelatine then stand the cup in a saucepan of barely simmering water until the gelatine has dissolved. Stir a little of the cheese and milk mixture into the gelatine then pour back into the cheese mixture. Leave until thick and beginning to set.

Whisk the egg whites together with the cream of tartar until peaking. Using a metal spoon fold the egg whites into the setting mixture. Spoon on top of the sponge base and chill until completely set.

To serve; transfer the cheesecake to a flat serving plate and slide off the paper.

Variation:

You can decorate the Cheesecake with a variety of fresh or canned fruits, but remember to add the Selections as necessary.

Raspberry Mousse

1 lb 8 oz (720 g) raspberries,
    fresh or frozen
4 oz (120 g) curd cheese
12 oz (360 g) fromage frais
4 tbs raspberry conserve
1 oz (30 g) caster sugar
1 tbs lemon juice
¼ tsp vanilla essence
¼ pint (150 ml) skimmed milk
2 tbs gelatine
2 large egg whites
pinch of cream of tartar

SELECTIONS PER SERVING:

½ Fruit
1 Protein
65 Optional Calories

CALORIES PER
SERVING: 135

SERVES 8

PREPARATION AND COOKING TIME: 20 MINUTES PLUS SETTING

Process 1 lb (480 g) of the raspberries, the curd cheese and fromage frais in a liquidiser or food processor, to a purée. Add the conserve, sugar, lemon juice and vanilla essence and process once again.

Pour the purée through a sieve into a bowl, pressing the pips firmly against the side of the sieve to extract as much of the juices as possible. Stir in about half the milk.

Pour the remaining milk into a cup or small bowl, sprinkle in the gelatine, stir well then stand the cup in a saucepan of barely simmering water until the gelatine has completely dissolved. Spoon a little of the purée into the gelatine then pour into the raspberry purée. Leave until beginning to set.

Whisk the egg whites and cream of tartar until peaking, fold one tablespoon into the purée to lighten the mixture then fold in the remainder.

Spoon the mixture into a pretty mould or glass bowl and chill in the refrigerator until completely set. To serve, if you have used a mould dip the mould briefly in hot water then invert on to a serving plate; decorate with the remaining raspberries.

Tip:

Always add a little of the cold mixture to the warm dissolved gelatine mixture, this will give a smooth gel. If making this recipe for a vegetarian; process the raspberries to a purée then cook with the setting agent according to the packaging instructions then continue as above.

Summer Pudding

1 lb (480 g) mixture of
  raspberries, loganberries,
  tayberries and blackberries
3 oz (90 g) caster sugar
5 oz (150 g) thin crustless white
  bread

SELECTIONS PER SERVING:

1 Bread
1 Fruit
110 Optional Calories

CALORIES PER
SERVING: 205

SERVES 4

PREPARATION: 15 MINUTES PLUS 1 HOUR STANDING
AND 6 HOURS CHILLING

NO COOKING REQUIRED

Rinse the fruit in cold water and place in a bowl, sprinkle with the sugar and stir to mix evenly. Leave for about an hour until the juices begin to flow from the berries.

Line a 1 pint (600 ml) pudding basin with the bread, slightly overlapping. Reserve sufficient bread to cover the top of the pudding. Spoon in the fruit and juices then cover with the remaining bread. Place a plate or saucer slightly smaller than the basin on top of the pudding and put several weights on top of the plate. Chill in the refrigerator overnight or for at least 6 hours.

To serve, invert the pudding on to a serving plate, remove the basin and cut into four wedges.

Tip:

Stand the weighted pudding on a plate to prevent any juices dripping on to the working surface or refrigerator.

Kirsch Fruit Salad

1 kiwi fruit, peeled, halved and
  cut into slices
½ small pineapple, skinned,
  cored and cut into cubes
6 oz (180 g) strawberries, sliced
5 oz (150 g) melon, cubed or
  shaped into balls
2 tsps caster sugar
3 tbs kirsch

SELECTIONS PER SERVING:

1 Fruit
50 Optional Calories

CALORIES PER
SERVING: 90

SERVES 4

PREPARATION: 10 MINUTES PLUS CHILLING

NO COOKING REQUIRED

Mix all the prepared fruit together in a serving bowl, add the sugar and kirsch and leave in a cool place to marinate for 3–4 hours.

Tip:

To check a melon is ripe; the melon should smell sweet and when pressed the skin should 'give' a little.

Summer Pudding

Chilled Lemon Soufflé (page 221)
and Kirsch Fruit Salad

Traditional Trifle

2 large eggs
1½ oz (45 g) caster sugar
1 oz (30 g) plain flour
½ tbs cornflour
½ pint (300 ml) skimmed milk
2–3 drops vanilla essence
4 tbs sherry
10 oz (300 g) raspberries
2 tsps toasted desiccated
   coconut

SELECTIONS PER SERVING:

½ Fruit
¼ Milk
½ Protein
90 Optional Calories

CALORIES PER
SERVING: 170

SERVES 4

PREPARATION AND COOKING TIME: 35 MINUTES PLUS COOLING

Pre-heat the oven to 180°C, 350°F, Gas Mark 4.

Line a 6 inch (15 cm) sandwich tin with non-stick baking parchment.

Break 1 egg into a bowl and add 1 oz (30 g) caster sugar. Place the bowl over a saucepan of simmering water and whisk until it becomes thick and creamy. Remove the bowl from the heat and whisk for a further 1–2 minutes to cool a little.

Sieve the flour and carefully fold into the mixture. Spoon into the lined tin – taking care to handle as little as possible. Bake in the pre-heated oven for about 15 minutes or until a light golden colour and firm to touch. Turn out of the tin, remove the lining paper and leave on a wire rack until cold.

Blend the cornflour with the milk, add 2–3 drops of vanilla essence and pour into a saucepan. Bring to the boil, stirring all the time. Remove from the heat and leave for 3 minutes to cool, stir well. Whisk the remaining egg and sugar together then pour into the hot milk and return to the heat. Stir over the lowest possible heat until the custard has thickened and will coat the back of a spoon. Remove from the heat and leave to cool.

Cut the cold sponge into four and place each piece in a sundae glass. Pour 1 tablespoon sherry over each sponge and arrange the raspberries on top. Pour over the cool custard and refrigerate until set.

Sprinkle each glass with the coconut and serve.

Variation:

The custard may be sweetened with artificial sweetener and the Optional Calories reduced to 45 per serving.

Orange and Pineapple Jelly Trifle

16 fl oz (480 ml) orange juice
1 sachet gelatine
artificial sweetener
8 oz (240 g) well-drained
    canned mixture of mandarins
    and pineapple chunks
2 tbs custard powder
1 tbs sugar
½ pint (300 ml) skimmed milk
½ oz (15 g) chopped toasted
    hazelnut kernels

SELECTIONS PER SERVING:

1½ Fruit
¼ Milk
50 Optional Calories

CALORIES PER
SERVING: 140

SERVES 4

PREPARATION AND COOKING TIME: 15 MINUTES PLUS CHILLING

Heat 4 fl oz (120 ml) of the orange juice, pour into a basin and sprinkle in the gelatine then stand in a saucepan of simmering water until the gelatine has dissolved. Stir in artificial sweetener to the equivalent of 2 tablespoons sugar.

Stir the dissolved gelatine mixture into the remaining orange juice which has been mixed with the fruit, pour into a serving bowl and leave until cold and set.

Blend the custard powder and sugar to a smooth paste with a little of the milk. Heat the remaining milk until steaming then pour into the custard powder paste. Bring to the boil, stirring all the time. Boil for 2 minutes then remove from the heat and cover with a damp piece of greaseproof paper or clingfilm (it should be directly over the custard to prevent a skin forming). Leave until cool.

Stir the cool custard then spoon over the set jelly. Sprinkle over the toasted nuts and serve.

Variation:

Substitute the gelatine with a vegetable-based gelling agent when preparing this recipe for vegetarians.

Mixed Fruit Fondue

2 medium mangoes
8 oz (240 g) fromage frais
2 tsps lemon juice
¼–½ tsp orange flower water
1 tbs frozen concentrated
 orange juice, thawed
2 tbs single cream
6 oz (180 g) strawberries, halved
 if large
2 kiwi fruits, peeled and cut into
 segments
6 oz (180 g) large black grapes,
 halved and deseeded

SELECTIONS PER SERVING:

1½ Fruit
½ Protein
25 Optional Calories

CALORIES PER
SERVING: 100

SERVES 6
PREPARATION: 15 MINUTES
NO COOKING REQUIRED

To prepare the mangoes, cut each mango lengthways down the broadside about ½ inch (1.25 cm) off-centre, then cut through the other side, the same distance from the centre, so the long thin stone can be removed. Using a spoon scrape the flesh from each mango half and from round each stone into a liquidiser. Add the fromage frais, lemon juice, orange flower water, orange juice and cream and process to a purée.

Divide the purée between six small ramekins. Place each ramekin in the centre of a small serving plate, arrange the prepared fruit decoratively round it and serve.

Variation:

If you prefer you can add only half a tablespoon of the cream to the liquidiser and use the remainder to swirl decoratively on the top of each fondue.

Vanilla Ice Cream with Black Cherry Sauce

1 lb 2 oz (540 g) sweet dark
 cherries, stoned
4 fl oz (120 ml) red wine
2 inch (5 cm) stick of cinnamon
3 inch (7.5 cm) strip of orange
 zest
1 oz (30 g) sugar
½ tbs arrowroot
3 tbs water
4 × 2 oz (60 g) scoops vanilla
 ice cream

SELECTIONS PER SERVING:

1 Fruit
160 Optional Calories

SERVES 4
PREPARATION AND COOKING TIME: 20 MINUTES PLUS CHILLING

Place the cherries in a saucepan with the wine, cinnamon and orange zest, cover and simmer for 10 minutes. Stir in the sugar and remove from the heat.

Blend the arrowroot to a paste with the water, stir into the cherries and wine and return to the heat. Bring to the boil, stirring all the time, boil for 1 minute then remove from the heat.

Chill the cherry sauce until cold. Remove the cinnamon and orange zest.

CALORIES PER
SERVING: 200

To serve, place the ice cream in four serving glasses, pour over the cherry sauce and serve immediately.

Tip:

Remove the orange zest with a potato peeler to avoid any bitter white pith remaining on the zest.

Below: Vanilla Ice Cream with Black Cherry Sauce

Moroccan Salad

1 medium orange
1 medium grapefruit
2 tbs sugar
¼ tsp orange flower water
8 medium kumquats, halved
4 oz (120 g) fresh dates, halved,
   stoned then cut lengthways

SELECTIONS PER SERVING:

2 Fruit
30 Optional Calories

CALORIES PER
SERVING: 100

SERVES 4
PREPARATION AND COOKING TIME: 15 MINUTES PLUS COOLING

To prepare the fruit, remove the zest from half the orange with a zester, squeeze the juice and pour into a measuring jug. Using a sharp knife cut the skin and pith from the grapefruit then cut between the membranes to remove all the segments. Pour any juice which drips from the fruit during preparation into the measuring jug with the orange juice. Make up to 4 fl oz (120 ml) with water.

Pour the juice into a small saucepan, add the sugar and heat gently until the sugar has dissolved. Increase the heat and boil fiercely for 3 minutes. Remove from the heat, allow to cool a little then add the orange flower water.

Place all the prepared fruit in an attractive bowl, pour over the orange syrup and leave until cold then refrigerate until ready to serve.

Tip:

If available use the pink-fleshed variety of grapefruit, they are sweeter than the ordinary fruit and look very attractive.

Blackcurrant Sorbet

For the purée:
10 oz (300 g) blackcurrants,
   stalks removed
4 tbs water
For the syrup:
6 fl oz (180 ml) water
4 oz (120 g) sugar
2 egg whites
pinch of cream of tartar

SELECTIONS PER SERVING:

105 Optional Calories

SERVES 6
PREPARATION AND COOKING TIME: 20 MINUTES
FREEZING TIME: 8 HOURS

Place the currants in a saucepan with 4 tablespoons water and simmer over a low to moderate heat for 5–8 minutes or until cooked. Transfer the blackcurrants and their juice to a liquidiser and process until smooth. Sieve, pressing the pulp against the sieve to remove as much juice as possible.

Illustrated on page 110

CALORIES PER
SERVING: 105

To make the syrup: heat the water and sugar gently until the sugar has dissolved, then boil rapidly for 2 minutes. Allow to cool, then stir into the sieved blackcurrant purée.

Freeze the blackcurrant mixture for about 3 hours, stirring from time to time until a 'slushy' consistency is obtained.

Whisk the egg whites and cream of tartar until peaking. Gently fold through the half-frozen blackcurrant mixture with a metal spoon. Return to the freezer for several hours or overnight.

Tip:

For a special occasion serve this sorbet in tall glasses with redcurrants hanging from the side of each glass.

2 medium pink grapefruit
2 medium oranges
1 lemon
4 fl oz (120 ml) boiling water
For the syrup:
3½ oz (105 g) sugar
4 fl oz (120 ml) water
2 egg whites
pinch of cream of tartar
sprigs of mint to garnish
   (optional)

SELECTIONS PER SERVING:

1 Fruit
75 Optional Calories

CALORIES PER
SERVING: 90

Grapefruit and Orange Sherbet

SERVES 6
PREPARATION AND COOKING TIME: 20 MINUTES
PLUS COOLING AND FREEZING

Use a potato peeler to remove the zest from the grapefruit, oranges and lemon. Put the zest in a basin and pour on the boiling water then leave until cool. Squeeze the juice from all the fruit and place in the refrigerator.

To make the syrup put the sugar in a saucepan with the cold water and heat gently until the sugar has dissolved then increase the heat and boil rapidly for 2 minutes.

Strain the water from the fruit zest and stir into the chilled fruit juice. Add the warm syrup and freeze for about 3 hours, stirring from time to time, until a 'slushy' consistency is obtained.

Whisk the egg whites and cream of tartar until peaking and fold into the half-frozen fruit mixture. Return to the freezer and freeze for several hours or overnight.

To serve, scoop into serving glasses and garnish with sprigs of mint.

Tip:

This recipe looks particularly attractive served with Blackcurrant Sorbet (see above).

Right: Blackcurrant Sorbet (page 108) and Grapefruit and Orange Sherbet (page 109)

Far right: Cheese and Yogurt Vanilla Mousse

8 oz (240 g) curd cheese
2 oz (60 g) caster sugar
few drops of vanilla essence
3 tbs hot water
1 tbs gelatine
10 fl oz (300 ml) low fat natural yogurt
3 large egg whites
pinch of cream of tartar
2 kiwi fruit, peeled and sliced
6 oz (180 g) strawberries, sliced

SELECTIONS PER SERVING:

½ Fruit
½ Milk
1 Protein
85 Optional Calories

CALORIES PER
SERVING: 220

Cheese and Yogurt Vanilla Mousse

SERVES 4
PREPARATION AND COOKING TIME: 15 MINUTES PLUS CHILLING

Beat together the curd cheese, sugar and vanilla essence.

Spoon the hot water into a cup or small basin, sprinkle on the gelatine and stir. Stand the cup or basin in a saucepan of barely simmering water until the gelatine has dissolved.

Gradually beat the yogurt into the curd cheese mixture. Stir a little of the curd cheese and yogurt into the dissolved gelatine, pour into the remaining curd cheese mixture.

Whisk the egg whites together with the cream of tartar until peaking. Fold into the cheese mixture using a metal spoon.

Spoon the mousse into four dessert dishes and leave until set. To serve, arrange the kiwi fruit and the strawberries on each mousse.

Tip:

When using dissolved gelatine always add a little of the mixture to the gelatine then, when evenly combined, stir the gelatine into the remaining mixture. This should prevent the gelatine forming little globules or strings.

8 large digestive biscuits
3 tbs margarine
3 tbs hot water
1 sachet gelatine
10 oz (300 g) curd cheese
3 oz (90 g) caster sugar
¼ pint (150 ml) skimmed milk
1 tbs lemon juice
1 lb 4 oz (600 g) blackberries
1 large egg white
pinch of cream of tartar

SELECTIONS PER SERVING:

1 Bread
1 Fat
½ Fruit
½ Protein
70 Optional Calories

CALORIES PER
SERVING: 235

Blackberry Cheesecake

SERVES 8

PREPARATION AND COOKING TIME: 20 MINUTES
PLUS CHILLING AND SETTING

Place the biscuits in a plastic bag and crush with a rolling pin to make crumbs. Melt the margarine in a small saucepan and stir in the biscuit crumbs. Press the crumbs into a 7 inch (17.5 cm) springform cake tin.

Spoon the hot water into a cup or small basin, sprinkle in the gelatine and stand the cup in a saucepan of barely simmering water until the gelatine has dissolved.

Process the curd cheese, sugar, milk, lemon juice and the blackberries (reserving a few for decoration) in a liquidiser or food processor until smooth. (If you wish sieve a little of the mixture to remove some of the pips.)

Whisk the egg white with the cream of tartar until peaking.

Spoon the blackberry and cheese mixture into a bowl, stir in the dissolved gelatine and mix well then fold in the whisked egg white. Spoon the mixture on top of the biscuit base and chill well until set.

To serve; remove the sides of the cake tin and slip the cheesecake on to a flat serving plate. Decorate with the reserved blackberries.

Variation:

If you prefer, use a mixture of berries such as raspberries, tayberries and loganberries.

Winter Pudding

5 oz (150 g) thin crustless slices
   of bread
10 oz (300 g) canned crushed
   pineapple
8 oz (240 g) canned mandarins
3 oz (90 g) dried apricots,
   roughly chopped
4 tsps caster sugar
¼ tsp ground ginger
2½ tsps arrowroot

SELECTIONS PER SERVING:

1 Bread
1½ Fruit
70 Optional Calories

CALORIES PER
SERVING: 205

SERVES 4

PREPARATION: 15 MINUTES

PLUS 6–7 HOURS CHILLING

NO COOKING REQUIRED

Line a 1¼ pint (750 ml) basin with the bread slightly overlapping the joins and leaving sufficient to cover the top.

Spoon the crushed pineapple into a sieve resting over a bowl. Allow the juice to run from the fruit, reserve 4 fl oz (120 ml) of juice and mix the remainder with the pineapple. Drain the mandarins, add the juice to the reserved pineapple juice, add the mandarins to the crushed pineapple. Stir in the apricots with 3 teaspoons caster sugar and the ground ginger.

Spoon the fruit into the lined basin and cover with the remaining bread. Lay a saucer or plate, slightly smaller than the top of the basin, over the pudding. Place several weights on the saucer or plate then leave in a cool place for 6–7 hours or overnight.

Blend a little of the fruit juice with the arrowroot, heat the remaining juice until steaming. Stir the arrowroot mixture into the steaming liquid and bring to the boil, stirring all the time, boil for 1 minute. Sweeten with the remaining teaspoon of sugar. Leave until cold.

To serve, invert the pudding on to the serving plate, remove the basin, cut into wedges and serve with the cold sauce.

Tip:

Stand the weighted basin on a large plate to catch any juices which may drip from the pudding during its soaking time.

12 oz (360 g) drained canned
    pears, plus 3 tbs juice
1 sachet gelatine
2–3 tsps lemon juice
good pinch of ground ginger
8 fl oz (240 ml) white grape
    juice
artificial sweetener (optional)
6 oz (180 g) fromage frais

SELECTIONS PER SERVING:

1 Fruit
½ Protein
30 Optional Calories

CALORIES PER
SERVING: 95

Pear and Grape Jelly

SERVES 4

PREPARATION AND COOKING TIME: 10 MINUTES PLUS SETTING

Spoon the pear juice into a cup or small basin, stir in the gelatine and stand in a saucepan of barely simmering water until the gelatine has completely dissolved.

Place the pears, 2 teaspoons lemon juice, ginger and grape juice in a liquidiser and process to a purée. Add more lemon juice and a little artificial sweetener, if desired, to taste.

Stir the dissolved gelatine into the pear and grape purée, allow to cool then stir in the fromage frais and pour into four serving glasses. Chill until set.

Variation:

This recipe may be used as a topping for fresh fruit. For example, chop 1 medium mango together with 6 oz (180 g) fresh strawberries, arrange in a bowl, then pour over the setting Pear and Grape Jelly. The Selections would then be: 2 Fruit, ½ Protein, 15 Optional Calories and the Total Calories per serving 135.

---

16 fl oz (480 ml) orange juice
4 tsps caster sugar
1 sachet gelatine
grated zest and juice of 1 lemon
5 fl oz (150 ml) low fat natural
    yogurt
8 oz (240 g) drained canned
    mandarin segments

SELECTIONS PER SERVING:

1½ Fruit
¼ Milk
20 Optional Calories

Saint Clements Special

SERVES 4

PREPARATION AND COOKING TIME: 15 MINUTES PLUS SETTING

Spoon 4 tablespoons orange juice into a cup or small basin (chill the remaining juice). Sprinkle the caster sugar and gelatine into the cup or basin, stir well then place in a saucepan of barely simmering water until the sugar and gelatine have dissolved.

Stir the lemon zest and juice into the chilled orange juice. Stir in the dissolved gelatine. Pour into four ¼ pint (150 ml) moulds and chill in the refrigerator until set.

CALORIES PER
SERVING: 110

To serve: dip the moulds into hot water and invert on to two serving plates. Spoon the yogurt round each jelly and arrange the mandarin segments on top of the yogurt.

Variation:

The orange juice can be substituted with pineapple or other juices but it may be necessary to sweeten the mixture with a little artificial sweetener.

Below: St Clements Special

Raspberry and Orange Granita

1 lb 8 oz (720 g) raspberries, fresh or frozen

2 tbs frozen concentrated orange juice, thawed

4 fl oz (120 ml) water

4 oz (120 g) sugar

SELECTIONS PER SERVING:

1 Fruit
90 Optional Calories

CALORIES PER SERVING: 120

SERVES 6

PREPARATION AND COOKING TIME: 30 MINUTES

Process the raspberries in a liquidiser or food processor to a purée. Push the raspberries through a sieve to extract as much juice as possible – this will take some time. There should be just over 1 pint (600 ml) of raspberry purée. Stir in the orange juice.

Gently heat the water together with the sugar until dissolved, pour into the fruit purée then pour into ice-cube trays, place in the freezer and freeze.

Just before serving remove the ice-cubes from the freezer, set aside for about 10 minutes then process in a food processor until 'slushy'. Spoon into six dessert glasses and serve immediately.

Variation:

To make a cheesy granita add 6 oz (180 g) curd cheese to the food processor when the mixture has been processed to a purée, process once again and then serve. Add ½ Protein to the Selections and increase Total Calories per serving to 170.

N.B. If the granita is to be made in advance it is essential it is frozen in ice-cube trays or the mixture will not be suitable for processing. If it is to be made just a few hours prior to serving it is possible to freeze it in any freezerproof container but check the mixture doesn't freeze too hard, stir it well every 30 minutes.

Sherry and Orange Custard Cream

2 medium oranges
2 tbs dry sherry
2 eggs, separated
½ pint (300 ml) skimmed milk
1 oz (30 g) caster sugar
¼ tsp ground cinnamon
1 tbs gelatine
4 tbs whipped dessert topping
1–2 tsps lemon juice
pinch of cream of tartar

SELECTIONS PER SERVING:

½ Fruit
¼ Milk
½ Protein
70 Optional Calories

CALORIES PER
SERVING: 160

SERVES 4

PREPARATION AND COOKING TIME: 25 MINUTES

Grate the zest from one orange and set aside.

Cut the peel from both oranges and cut into segments catching any juices. Cut the segments into ½ inch (1.25 cm) pieces. Sprinkle the orange with the sherry and place in the refrigerator.

Whisk together the egg yolks, milk, caster sugar and cinnamon. Pour into the top of a double saucepan or into a bowl resting over a saucepan of simmering water. Heat, stirring all the time, until the mixture is steaming and has thickened (about 15 minutes).

Sprinkle the gelatine over the sauce and stir well until dissolved. Pour the sauce into a bowl and leave until cool then transfer to the refrigerator and chill for at least 30 minutes.

Just before serving stir the marinated orange together with its juices and lemon juice into the chilled custard, fold in the whipped topping.

Whisk the egg whites with the cream of tartar until peaking, carefully fold into the custard and spoon into a serving dish. Sprinkle over the orange zest and chill until completely set.

Variation:

For an even creamier flavour substitute the dessert topping with 4 tablespoons whipped double cream. The Optional Calories will remain the same.

WINTER WARMERS

Few meals are more comforting than a bowl of piping hot homemade soup or a hearty stew. And you'll find that all the recipes in this section are satisfying, warming and nourishing and therefore particularly welcome on an icy winter's day. Some recipes such as Lancashire Hot Pot on page 130 or Shepherd's Pie (see page 143) are variations of traditional favourites. Others, such as Paprika Quorn with Tomatoes and Baby Corn (page 142) or Stuffed Cabbage Leaves with Sauerkraut (page 133), incorporate comparatively new or Continental ingredients.

Hot crisp-skinned jacket potatoes make a particularly good accompaniment to stews and casseroles. Scrub a few potatoes and bake them in the oven while any of the casseroles are cooking or, if you have a microwave oven, you may prefer to cook one or two potatoes quickly in the microwave.

All the recipes are suitable for family meals, and can be enjoyed at any time throughout the year. The Braised Beef with Winter Vegetables (page 134) makes a simple warming meal, especially when entertaining guests. Like many of the recipes in the MADE TO MEASURE COOK BOOK, the Lentil Bolognaise (page 136) can be frozen in individual portions to be eaten later. You can even freeze the Apple and Plum Filled Pancakes (see page 145), so long as you freeze the pancakes separately interleaved with sheets of foil or freezerwrap.

Although these recipes are called Winter Warmers don't forget there are many other recipes in the MADE TO MEASURE COOK BOOK that are just as enjoyable to eat during the cold winter months.

Yellow Split Pea and Ham Soup

4 oz (120 g) yellow split peas
2 tsps margarine
1 large onion, chopped
4 oz (120 g) carrot, sliced
2 oz (60 g) boiled cooked ham, diced
¼ tsp dried sage
pinch of ground allspice
1 pint (600 ml) chicken or vegetable stock
1 tbs chopped fresh parsley to garnish

SELECTIONS PER SERVING:

1 Bread
½ Fat
½ Protein
¾ Vegetable

CALORIES PER SERVING: 150

Illustrations on previous page: Shepherds Pie (page 143) and Chicken Casserole with Tarragon Dumplings (page 141)

SERVES 4

PREPARATION AND COOKING TIME: 45 MINUTES PLUS SOAKING

Cover the split peas with cold water and leave to soak for several hours or overnight. Drain the peas and transfer to a saucepan, cover with cold water and bring to the boil, boil rapidly for 10 minutes.

Heat the margarine in a saucepan and stir-fry the onion for 1–2 minutes, cover the saucepan and leave over a low heat for a further 4–5 minutes. Stir in the carrots, ham, sage and allspice. Drain the split peas and stir into the saucepan together with the stock. Bring to the boil, reduce the heat, cover and simmer gently for 30–35 minutes until the peas are cooked.

Ladle the soup into warm bowls, sprinkle with the chopped parsley and serve.

Tip:

If you have boiled the ham yourself skim the fat from the surface of the cooking liquid, add a little chicken stock and use in the soup.

Minestrone Soup

4 tsps oil
2 cloves garlic, finely chopped
1 onion, chopped
1 large carrot, chopped
3 sticks celery, chopped
4 oz (120 g) courgettes, chopped
16 fl oz (480 ml) tomato juice
1 pint (600 ml) vegetable stock
6 oz (180 g) cooked ham, diced
12 oz (360 g) drained canned kidney beans
1 tsp dried basil
good pinch of dried oregano
4 oz (120 g) macaroni
2 tbs chopped fresh parsley
1 oz (30 g) Parmesan cheese, finely grated

SERVES 4

PREPARATION AND COOKING TIME: 45 MINUTES

Heat the oil in a saucepan and stir-fry the garlic and onion for 2–3 minutes; do not allow the garlic to brown. Stir in the carrot, celery and courgettes, cover, reduce the heat and leave for 4–5 minutes to steam. Pour the tomato juice and stock into the saucepan. Add the ham, kidney beans and herbs. Bring to the boil, reduce the heat and simmer for 20 minutes.

Add the macaroni and parsley to the saucepan, stir well and simmer for 10 minutes or until the pasta is cooked. Adjust the seasoning then ladle into four warm bowls. Sprinkle over the Parmesan cheese and serve.

SELECTIONS PER SERVING:

2 Bread
1 Fat
1½ Protein
1½ Vegetable
15 Optional Calories

CALORIES PER
SERVING: 350

Variation:

The ham may be omitted or substituted with diced smoked tofu or extra kidney beans but remember to alter the Selections as necessary.

4 × 8–9 oz (240–270 g) Spanish
   onions, peeled
1 oz (30 g) walnut or pecan
   kernels, finely chopped
1 oz (30 g) fresh wholemeal
   breadcrumbs
2 oz (60 g) strong-flavoured
   hard cheese, e.g. mature
   Cheddar, sage Derby, grated
salt and pepper
½ tbs oil

SELECTIONS PER SERVING:

½ Fat
1 Protein
3 Vegetable
25 Optional Calories

CALORIES PER
SERVING: 150

Cheese and Nut Stuffed Onions

SERVES 4

PREPARATION AND COOKING TIME: I HOUR I5 MINUTES

Pre-heat the oven to 190°C, 375°F, Gas Mark 5.

Cut a very thin slice from the root end of the onions, plunge into boiling water and boil for about 30 minutes until just cooked, take care not to overcook. Remove from the water, allow to drain and cool a little. Using a small sharp knife, cut a thin slice from the top of each onion and then using a teaspoon remove a proportion of the inside, leaving sufficient flesh to maintain the shape.

Chop the scooped-out onion and mix together with the nuts, bread-crumbs and cheese. Season with a little salt and pepper. Spoon the stuffing back into each onion, pressing it down gently. Pile any remaining stuffing on top.

Line a baking sheet with a piece of foil and brush with a little oil. Place the onions on the foil and brush them with the remaining oil. Bake in the pre-heated oven for 25–30 minutes.

Tip:

Spanish onions have a mild, slightly sweet flavour so they are ideal for stuffing, incorporating in salads or serving as an accompaniment to main meals.

Celery Soup with Tofu

2 tsps margarine
1 onion, chopped
1 lb 2 oz–1 lb 4 oz (540–600 g)
   celery, sliced
1 oz (30 g) flour
3–4 tsps chopped fresh chervil
1 pint (600 ml) vegetable stock
½ pint (300 ml) skimmed milk
salt and pepper
lemon juice
5 oz (150 g) smoked tofu, cut
   into small cubes

SELECTIONS PER SERVING:

½ Fat
¼ Milk
½ Protein
2 Vegetable
25 Optional Calories

CALORIES PER
SERVING: 115

SERVES 4

PREPARATION AND COOKING TIME: 45 MINUTES

Melt the margarine in a saucepan and stir-fry the onion for 4 minutes. Mix in the celery, sprinkle in the flour and stir well. Add the chervil and stock and bring to the boil, stirring all the time. Reduce the heat, cover the saucepan and simmer for 20–25 minutes.

Process the celery mixture in a liquidiser or food processor until smooth. Return the celery purée to the saucepan, stir in the milk and season to taste with salt, pepper and lemon juice.

Add the smoked tofu to the soup and stir over a moderate heat. Pour into warm soup bowls and serve.

Tip:

Make this soup when celery is in season and cheap. It freezes well but the tofu should be added when the soup is reheated.

Celery Soup with Tofu

Chinese Vegetables with Tofu

3 oz (90 g) onion, finely
   chopped
2 cloves garlic, crushed
1 tsp finely chopped ginger
6 tbs soy sauce
4 tbs lemon juice
2 tbs dry sherry
2 tsps sesame oil
2 tsps clear honey
1 lb 8 oz (720 g) firm tofu, cut
   into 1 inch (2.5 cm) cubes
4 tsps oil
6 oz (180 g) button mushrooms,
   sliced
3 oz (90 g) Chinese cabbage,
   shredded
1 large red pepper, deseeded
   and cut into 1 inch (2.5 cm)
   squares
6 oz (180 g) beansprouts
3 oz (90 g) spring onions, cut
   into diagonal slices

SELECTIONS PER SERVING:

1½ Fat
2 Protein
2½ Vegetable
20 Optional Calories

CALORIES PER
SERVING: 215

SERVES 4

PREPARATION AND COOKING TIME: 35 MINUTES PLUS MARINATING

Prepare the marinade: mix together the onion, garlic, ginger, soy sauce, lemon juice, sherry, sesame oil and honey. Add the tofu and turn to coat. Cover and chill for 4 hours, or longer, turning the tofu occasionally.

Heat the oil in a saucepan, large frying pan or wok. Drain the tofu and add to the pan. Stir-fry over a high heat for 2–3 minutes. Pour the marinade into a small saucepan and leave over a low heat.

Mix the mushrooms and cabbage into the frying pan or wok and stir-fry for a further 2–3 minutes. Add the red pepper, beansprouts, spring onions and 2 tablespoons of the warm marinade. Continue stir-frying over a moderate heat for 2 minutes. Transfer the tofu and vegetables to a warm serving plate and pour the marinade into a small jug to serve separately.

Chinese Vegetables with Tofu

Turkey and Mushroom Pie

For the pastry:
3½ oz (105 g) plain flour
3 tbs margarine
1 tsp skimmed milk
For the filling:
1 tbs oil
1 large onion, chopped
**1 red pepper, deseeded and cut
    into strips**
**14 oz (420 g) boned and skinned
    turkey, cut into 1 inch
    (2.5 cm) cubes**
6 oz (180 g) mushrooms, sliced
1 oz (30 g) flour
½ pint (300 ml) stock
**2 oz (60 g) frozen sliced beans,
    thawed**

SELECTIONS PER SERVING:

1 Bread
2 Fat
3 Protein
1½ Vegetable
50 Optional Calories

CALORIES PER
SERVING: 380

SERVES 4

PREPARATION AND COOKING TIME: 1 HOUR 20 MINUTES PLUS COOLING

Pre-heat the oven to 200°C, 400°F, Gas Mark 6.

To make the pastry; reserve 2–3 teaspoons flour, sieve the remainder into a mixing bowl. Add the margarine (if possible margarine which has been stored in the freezer) and rub into the flour with your fingertips until the mixture resembles fresh breadcrumbs. Using a round-bladed knife mix 1 tablespoon ice-cold water into the flour and margarine to form a smooth dough. Wrap the pastry in clingfilm and refrigerate for 15 minutes while preparing the filling.

Heat the oil in a saucepan and stir-fry the onion and pepper for 3–4 minutes. Add the turkey and stir round until it loses its pinkness. Add the mushrooms and sprinkle in the flour. Gradually blend in the stock and bring to the boil, stirring all the time, cover and reduce the heat and simmer gently for 20 minutes, stirring occasionally. Leave to cool.

Place a pie funnel in the centre of a 2 pint (1.2 litre) pie dish. Stir the sliced beans into the cool turkey mixture then spoon into the pie dish.

Sprinkle the work surface and rolling pin with the reserved flour. Roll out the pastry a little larger than the pie dish. Cut a strip all round, moisten the edge of the pie dish and press the pastry strip firmly on to it, brush with cold water. Lay the pastry lid on top and press firmly on to the pastry edge. Trim off any excess pastry from the edge and press round the pie with the prongs of a fork. Brush with the milk.

Place the pie on a baking sheet and bake in the pre-heated oven for 15 minutes then reduce the heat to 160°C, 325°F, Gas Mark 3 for a further 30 minutes.

Tip:

Freeze the pastry and turkey filling separately so they thaw and cook more quickly. For a rich golden brown pastry crust brush with 1–2 teaspoons beaten egg before baking, add 5 Optional Calories per person.

Chicken and Vegetable Pie

12–14 oz (360–420 g) cooked
  or frozen vegetables, cut into
  ¾ inch (2 cm) pieces
salt
6 oz (180 g) flour
3 oz (90 g) margarine
approximately 2 tbs ice-cold
  water
2 tbs cornflour
12 fl oz (360 ml) skimmed milk
¼ onion, grated
¼ chicken stock cube
10 oz (300 g) cooked chicken,
  cut into 1–1½ inch
  (2.5–4 cm) chunks
pepper
For rolling and completing:
2 tsps flour
2 tsps skimmed milk

SELECTIONS PER SERVING:

1½ Bread
2 Fat
¼ Milk
2½ Protein
1¼ Vegetable
125 Optional Calories

CALORIES PER
SERVING: 545

SERVES 4

PREPARATION AND COOKING TIME: 50 MINUTES

Pre-heat the oven to 200°C, 400°F, Gas Mark 6.

If using frozen vegetables cook in lightly salted water while making the pastry.

Sieve the flour into a mixing bowl, add the margarine (if possible margarine which has been stored in the freezer) and using your fingertips rub into the flour to form breadcrumbs. Using a round-bladed knife mix in the water to form a firm and smooth dough. Cover and refrigerate while preparing the pie filling.

Blend the cornflour to a smooth paste with a little milk. Pour the remaining milk into a saucepan, add the onion and crumble in the stock cube. Heat until steaming then pour on to the blended cornflour, stir well, return to the saucepan and bring to the boil stirring all the time. Boil for 1–2 minutes. Drain the vegetables and stir into the sauce. Add the chicken and season to taste with salt and pepper.

Dust a working surface with the 2 teaspoons flour. Roll the pastry out on the surface using light strokes of the rolling pin. Roll out until about ½ inch (1.25 cm) larger than a 2 pint (1.2 litre) pie dish.

Spoon the sauce into the pie dish and dampen the edge with cold water. Cut the ½ inch (1.25 cm) border from the pastry and press on to the rim. Cut a large oval from the centre of the pastry, about 4½ inch (11.25 cm) long and 3 inch (7.5 cm) wide (put aside to use for another recipe). Lift the oval out of the pastry and weigh it, it should weigh 3 oz (90 g). Carefully place the pastry lid on top of the pie and press well on to the edging. Using a round-bladed knife flake the edge. Stand the pie dish on a baking sheet, brush with the milk and bake in the pre-heated oven for 25 minutes until the pastry is golden and the filling bubbling.

Tip:

Use the pastry trimmings 3 oz (90 g) for the Rhubarb and Apple Lattice (see page 148). The pastry freezes well; place in a plastic bag and label clearly.

Chicken and Vegetable Pie *illustrated overleaf*

Pork and Cider Cobbler

1 lb (480 g) pork tenderloin
1 medium dessert apple, sliced
1 red pepper, deseeded, halved
and sliced
4 oz (120 g) frozen peas
½ pint (300 ml) cider
1 oz (30 g) cornflour
4 oz (120 g) plain flour
1½ tsps baking powder
½ tsp mixed dried herbs
4 tsps margarine
4–5 tbs skimmed milk

SELECTIONS PER SERVING:

1½ Bread
1 Fat
3 Protein
¾ Vegetable
45 Optional Calories

CALORIES PER
SERVING: 390

SERVES 4

PREPARATION AND COOKING TIME: 55 MINUTES

Pre-heat the oven to 220°C, 425°F, Gas Mark 7.

Place the pork on the rack of a grill pan and cook, turning once, until the fat has stopped dripping from the meat.

Cut the pork into 1½ inch (4 cm) cubes and place in a saucepan with the apple, pepper and peas. Stir in the cider, cover and simmer over a low heat for 30 minutes.

Blend the cornflour to a paste with a little water, set aside.

Reserve ½ tablespoon flour, sieve the remainder with the baking powder into a mixing bowl, stir in the mixed herbs. Add the margarine (if possible margarine which has been stored in the freezer) and rub into the flour with your fingertips until the mixture resembles fresh breadcrumbs. Using a round-bladed knife gradually mix 4 tablespoons milk into the flour mixture to form a soft dough, if necessary add a little more milk.

Left: Chicken and Vegetable Pie
Right: Pork and Cider Cobbler

Sprinkle the reserved flour over the work surface and rolling pin. Roll out the dough until ½–¾ inch (1.25–2 cm) thick, cut into six triangles. Leave to stand for about 10 minutes.

Stir the blended cornflour into the cider and pork mixture and bring to the boil, simmer for 1–2 minutes, stirring all the time.

Transfer the pork mixture to a deep ovenproof dish, arrange the scones on top and brush with a little milk. Bake in the pre-heated oven for about 15 minutes until the scones are golden brown.

Tip:

Use the scone topping on meat, fish or vegetable casseroles. Either leave them plain or brush with skimmed milk and sprinkle over 2 teaspoons sesame seeds but remember to add 10 Optional Calories per serving.

4 tsps margarine
1 onion, chopped
1 oz (30 g) flour
6 oz (180 g) mushrooms, sliced
1 oz (30 g) sliced cooked ham, cut into strips
1 lb (480 g) skinned and boned chicken thighs
12 fl oz (360 ml) chicken stock
½ tsp dried tarragon
salt and pepper

SELECTIONS PER SERVING:

1 Fat
3 Protein
¾ Vegetable
35 Optional Calories

CALORIES PER
SERVING: 210

Chicken, Ham and Mushroom Casserole

SERVES 4

PREPARATION AND COOKING TIME: 1 HOUR 20 MINUTES

Pre-heat the oven to 180°C, 350°F, Gas Mark 4.

Heat the margarine in a flameproof casserole and stir-fry the onion for 4 minutes then sprinkle in the flour and stir well. Remove from the heat. Stir the mushrooms, ham and chicken into the casserole. Gradually blend in the stock and season with the tarragon, salt and pepper.

Bring to the boil, stirring all the time, cover and bake in the pre-heated oven for 1 hour.

Tip:

If the chicken thighs are large cut them in half then add to the casserole.

Pasta with Broccoli and Ham in Lentil Sauce

For the lentil sauce:

2 tsps oil

1 clove garlic, chopped

1 small onion, chopped

1 tbs tomato purée

6 oz (180 g) split red lentils

16 fl oz (480 ml) vegetable stock

salt and pepper

For the pasta:

6 oz (180 g) large shaped pasta e.g. shells, penne

8 oz (240 g) calabrese broccoli, stalks cut into ½ inch (1.25 cm) cubes, large florets divided into smaller pieces about the size of walnuts

2 tsps oil

1 red pepper, deseeded and sliced

6 oz (180 g) cooked lean ham, diced

SELECTIONS PER SERVING:

1½ Bread
1 Fat
3 Protein
1 Vegetable

CALORIES PER
SERVING: 400

SERVES 4

PREPARATION AND COOKING TIME: 40 MINUTES

To make the lentil sauce: heat the oil in a saucepan and stir-fry the garlic and onion for 3–4 minutes. Stir in the tomato purée, lentils and stock, bring to the boil, stir well then cover and leave over a low heat to simmer for 20 minutes.

While the lentil sauce is cooking prepare the pasta mixture: cook the pasta in boiling slightly salted water according to the packaging instructions. Plunge the broccoli in boiling water and cook for 3–4 minutes, drain. Heat the oil in a saucepan and stir-fry the red pepper for 3–4 minutes, add the drained broccoli and ham and stir-fry for a further 3 minutes. Drain the hot pasta and mix into the ham mixture. Spoon on to a warm serving dish or bowl.

Process the lentil sauce in a liquidiser or food processor until smooth, season to taste with salt and pepper. Pour the lentil sauce over the pasta and serve.

Variation:

8 oz (240 g) smoked tofu may be used in place of the ham, reduce the number of Protein Selections to 2½ per serving and the Total Calories per serving to 380.

14 oz (420 g) boneless lamb
10 oz (300 g) onions, chopped
3 oz (90 g) lamb's or ox kidney
½ pint (300 ml) vegetable stock
¼ tsp dried thyme
salt and pepper
1 lb 8 oz (720 g) potatoes, thinly
   sliced
1 tbs oil or margarine

SELECTIONS PER SERVING:

1½ Bread
½ Fat
3 Protein
¾ Vegetable
40 Optional Calories

CALORIES PER
SERVING: 395

Lancashire Hot Pot

SERVES 4

PREPARATION AND COOKING TIME: 2 HOURS 15 MINUTES

Pre-heat the oven to 180°C, 350°F, Gas Mark 4.

Place the lamb on the rack of a grill pan and cook under a moderate heat, turning once, until the fat has stopped dripping. Cut into 1½ inch (4 cm) pieces and place in a casserole dish. Scatter over the onions.

Halve the kidney, remove the white central core, wash well and cut into cubes. Add the kidney, stock and thyme to the casserole and season to taste with salt and pepper.

Arrange the potatoes on top of the meat and onions. Brush with oil or dot with margarine.

Bake in the pre-heated oven for 1¾ hours then increase the temperature to 220°C, 425°F, Gas Mark 7 for a further 15 minutes until the potatoes are golden brown.

Variation:

Vegetables can be added to the meat and onions but it may be necessary to increase the cooking time.

3 oz (90 g) thin boneless pork
   loin chop
½ tbs oil
¼ tsp cumin seeds
½ onion, thinly sliced
1 small stick celery, thinly sliced
1 oz (30 g) carrot, cut into
   1 × ¼ inch (2.5 cm × 5 mm)
   lengths
1 oz (30 g) mangetout, halved
¼–½ red or green pepper,
   deseeded and cut into 1 × ¼
   inch (2.5 cm × 5 mm) lengths
1 oz (30 g) beansprouts
soy sauce

Cumin Pork Stir-Fry

SERVES 1

PREPARATION AND COOKING TIME: 30 MINUTES

Grill the pork chop under a moderate heat, turning once, until the fat has stopped dripping from the meat and it is almost cooked.

Heat the oil in a non-stick or heavy-based small saucepan and stir-fry the cumin seeds and onion for 2–3 minutes or until the onion begins to soften.

Cut the pork into small pieces about the same size as the pepper and carrot.

Add the celery and carrot to the saucepan and stir-fry for a further 2 minutes. Add the pork, mangetout and pepper and cook, stirring

SELECTIONS PER SERVING:

1½ Fat
2 Protein
2 Vegetable

CALORIES PER
SERVING: 240

continuously for 2–3 minutes.

Stir the beansprouts into the saucepan, cover and leave over a moderate heat for 1–2 minutes. Add 2 teaspoons soy sauce, stir well then spoon on to a serving plate and serve with soy sauce to sprinkle over as desired.

Tip:

Cumin seeds have a distinctive flavour, if you do not like the pungent flavour omit them and add 1 finely chopped clove of garlic when frying the onion.

---

6 oz (180 g) sirloin or fillet
    steak, about 1 inch (2.5 cm)
    thick
2 tsps oil
½ red or yellow pepper,
    deseeded and cut into thin
    strips
1 bunch spring onions, cut into
    ¾ inch (2 cm) slices
½ tsp cornflour
5 tbs ginger wine
1–2 tsps lemon juice

SELECTIONS PER SERVING:

1 Fat
2½ Protein
¾ Vegetable
40 Optional Calories

CALORIES PER
SERVING: 225

Steak with Pepper and Spring Onions

SERVES 2

PREPARATION AND COOKING TIME: 15 MINUTES

Lay the steak on the rack of a grill pan and cook about 2½ inch (6.25 cm) away from the heat for about 7–8 minutes, turning once, until cooked but rare.

Heat the oil in a saucepan and stir-fry the pepper and spring onions over a medium heat for 4 minutes.

Blend the cornflour together with the ginger wine.

Transfer the steak to a chopping board and cut into very thin slices. Add the steak to the saucepan with the pepper and spring onions, pour in the ginger wine and cornflour and cook over a very high heat until the sauce is boiling and the steak is cooked to taste. Remove from the heat and add lemon juice to taste.

Tip:

While the steak is cooking put 3 oz (90 g) tagliatelle in boiling water and cook for 8–10 minutes, serve with the steak. Add 1½ Bread Selections to your meal and the Calories per serving will be 380.

Cassoulet

3 oz (90 g) dried haricot beans
2 tbs oil
10 oz (300 g) boned and skinned
  chicken thighs, cut into
  2 inch (5 cm) pieces
2 cloves garlic, finely chopped
1 large onion, thickly sliced
2 carrots, cut into 1½ inch
  (4 cm) chunks
4 tbs chopped fresh parsley
¼ tsp ground cloves
8 fl oz (240 ml) chicken stock
8 oz (240 g) canned chopped
  tomatoes
bay leaf
4 oz (120 g) cooked saveloy
  sausage
salt and pepper
parsley to garnish (optional)

SELECTIONS PER SERVING:

½ Bread
1½ Fat
3 Protein
1½ Vegetable
20 Optional Calories

CALORIES PER
SERVING: 290

SERVES 4

PREPARATION AND COOKING TIME: 2 HOURS PLUS SOAKING OVERNIGHT

Place the haricot beans in a bowl, cover with cold water and leave for several hours or overnight. The next morning drain the beans, place in a saucepan and cover with cold water. Bring to a rolling boil and cook for 15–20 minutes then drain.

Pre-heat the oven to 160°C, 325°F, Gas Mark 3.

Heat 1½ tablespoons oil in a large flameproof casserole and brown the chicken. Remove the chicken from the casserole, add the remaining oil and stir-fry the garlic and onion for 3 minutes. Add the carrots and stir-fry for a further 2–3 minutes. Return the chicken to the casserole and stir in all the remaining ingredients, except the saveloy sausage and salt and pepper. Bring to the boil over a moderate heat, stir well.

Cut the sausage into four pieces and place on top of the casserole. Cover the casserole and cook in the pre-heated oven for 1 hour 30 minutes. Remove the bay leaf from the casserole, season to taste with salt and pepper and sprinkle over a little parsley if desired.

Tip:

Always boil dried beans rapidly for at least 10 minutes after soaking and always season with salt when completely cooked.

Red Lentil and Vegetable Curry

4 tsps oil
1 large onion, finely chopped
2 cloves garlic, finely chopped
6 oz (180 g) carrot, diced
2 sticks celery, diced
4 tsps curry powder
15 oz (450 g) canned chopped
  tomatoes
8 oz (240 g) split red lentils
1 pint (600 ml) vegetable stock
lemon juice
salt and pepper

SERVES 4

PREPARATION AND COOKING TIME: 40 MINUTES

Heat the oil in a large saucepan and stir-fry the onion and garlic for 3 minutes. Add the carrot and celery and stir round then add the curry powder. Stir in the tomatoes, lentils and stock and bring to the boil over a moderate heat. Cover the saucepan, reduce the heat and simmer for 20–25 minutes, stirring occasionally, if necessary add a little more stock.

Season to taste with lemon juice, salt and pepper and serve.

SELECTIONS PER SERVING:

1 Fat
2 Protein
2½ Vegetable

CALORIES PER
SERVING: 200

5 oz (150 g) minced pork
5 oz (150 g) minced beef
2 cloves garlic, finely chopped
1 small onion, finely chopped
6 oz (180 g) cooked long grain
  rice
1 egg
2 tbs chopped fresh parsley
3 tsps paprika
½ tsp dried marjoram
salt and pepper
8 large cabbage leaves
9 oz (270 g) drained sauerkraut,
  rinsed
8 oz (240 g) canned chopped
  tomatoes
½ pint (300 ml) chicken stock

SELECTIONS PER SERVING:

½ Bread
2 Protein
2 Vegetable
15 Optional Calories

CALORIES PER
SERVING: 205

Variation:

Add more vegetables if desired. Cauliflower and swede will absorb the curry flavour well. Adjust the curry powder to suit your taste.

Stuffed Cabbage Leaves with Sauerkraut

SERVES 4
PREPARATION AND COOKING TIME: 1 HOUR 20 MINUTES

Pre-heat the oven to 180°C, 350°F, Gas Mark 4.

Form the pork and beef into four patties, place on the rack of a grill pan and cook, turning once, until the fat stops dripping from the meat. Allow to cool a little then crumble into a mixing bowl. Mix together with the garlic, onion, rice, egg, parsley, 2 teaspoons paprika and marjoram. Season to taste with salt and pepper.

Cut out a 'V' shape in the base of each cabbage leaf to remove the thickest part of the stem. Plunge the leaves into a saucepan of boiling water and cook for about 3 minutes or until limp, drain well.

Lay the cabbage leaves flat on the working surface and divide the meat mixture between them. Roll each leaf from the stem end to the top, tucking in the sides as you roll.

Mix the sauerkraut together with the tomatoes, chicken stock and remaining paprika then spread in an ovenproof dish large enough to hold the cabbage leaves. Arrange the stuffed leaves on top, stem end down, cover with a piece of foil and cook in the pre-heated oven for 50–60 minutes.

Tip:

Make sure the cabbage leaves have been cooked for long enough before stuffing them – the cooking time will vary considerably from one cabbage to another.

Braised Beef with Winter Vegetables

2½–3 lb (1.2–1.4 kg) topside –
   ask your butcher to prepare
   this without the usual
   covering of fat
2 tbs oil
8 oz (240 g) baby onions, peeled
4 large sticks celery, cut into
   3 inch (7.5 cm) lengths
1 lb 12 oz (840 g) mixture of
   root vegetables, e.g. swede,
   turnip, kohlrabi; cut into
   large chunks
9 oz (270 g) carrots, cut into
   large chunks
¾ pint (450 ml) beef stock
bouquet garni
4 tsps cornflour
2 tsps chopped fresh parsley to
   garnish

SELECTIONS PER SERVING:

1 Fat
3 Protein
2½ Vegetable
10 Optional Calories

CALORIES PER
SERVING: 250

SERVES 6

PREPARATION AND COOKING TIME: 3 HOURS 30 MINUTES

Pre-heat the oven to 160°C, 325°F, Gas Mark 3.

Place the topside on a grill rack and grill, turning from time to time until the fat stops dripping from the joint.

Heat the oil in a very large flameproof casserole and stir-fry the onions until beginning to brown. Add all the remaining vegetables and stir well then add the stock which should half cover the vegetables. Make a slight dip in the vegetables and lay the joint on the vegetable mixture. Add the bouquet garni.

Bring to the boil over a low heat. Cover tightly (if necessary weigh down the casserole lid) and place in the pre-heated oven for 2½–3 hours until the topside is tender.

Remove the joint and the vegetables with a draining spoon, discard the bouquet garni. Keep the meat and vegetables warm while completing the recipe. Blend the cornflour to a smooth paste with a little water then add to the stock in the casserole and bring to a rapid boil stirring all the time.

Either serve the beef as a whole joint or sliced, and surround with the vegetables sprinkled with parsley. Allow 3 oz (90 g) beef per person. Serve the gravy separately in a sauceboat.

Variation:

Parsnips may be added to the vegetable mixture but remember to add the additional Bread Selections or Optional Calories.

Vegetarian Chilli

4 tsps oil
1 large onion, chopped
1 green pepper, deseeded and
   chopped
½ tbs mustard seeds
2 × 15 oz (450 g) cans kidney
   beans, liquid reserved
15 oz (450 g) canned chopped
   tomatoes

SERVES 4

PREPARATION AND COOKING TIME: 1 HOUR

Heat the oil in a large saucepan and stir-fry the onion and green pepper for 7–8 minutes. Add the mustard seeds and stir-fry for another minute.

4 tbs tomato purée
½ tbs chilli powder
½ tsp cumin seeds
½ tsp cocoa
good pinch of cinnamon
salt and pepper
1 tomato, chopped
1½ oz (45 g) cucumber, diced
½–¾ oz (15–20 g) green chilli,
   seeds removed, thinly sliced
4 spring onions, thinly sliced
5 fl oz (150 ml) low fat natural
   yogurt
1 lime, cut into quarters, to
   garnish

SELECTIONS PER SERVING:

1 Fat
¼ Milk
2 Protein
3 Vegetable
5 Optional Calories

CALORIES PER
SERVING: 280

Stir in the kidney beans and their liquid, the canned tomatoes, tomato purée, chilli powder, cumin seeds, cocoa, cinnamon and salt and pepper. Bring to the boil, stir well then reduce the heat and simmer uncovered for 35–40 minutes, stirring frequently to prevent burning.

Divide the chilli between four warm bowls and top each serving with the chopped tomato, cucumber, chilli and spring onions. Spoon over the yogurt, garnish with the lime and serve.

Tip:

This recipe may be frozen without the vegetable and yogurt topping. Add a little extra stock or water when reheating.

Right: Braised Beef with Winter Vegetables

6 oz (180 g) pasta shapes
1 tbs margarine
12 oz (360 g) leeks, thickly
    sliced
1 tbs cornflour
½ pint (300 ml) skimmed milk
12 oz (360 g) Quorn
½ tsp Dijon mustard
2 oz (60 g) Danish blue cheese,
    grated or crumbled
2 tomatoes, sliced

SELECTIONS PER SERVING:

1½ Bread
½ Fat
¼ Milk
2 Protein
1 Vegetable
20 Optional Calories

CALORIES PER
SERVING: 350

Quorn and Leek Pasta Bake

SERVES 4

PREPARATION AND COOKING TIME: 55 MINUTES

Pre-heat the oven to 200°C, 400°F, Gas Mark 6.

Cook the pasta according to the packaging instructions until *al dente* (firm to bite).

Meanwhile melt the margarine in a saucepan, add the leeks and stir round then cover and cook gently over a low heat for 12 minutes until limp.

Blend the cornflour together with the milk. Drain the hot pasta.

Stir the cornflour and milk into the leeks and bring to the boil stirring all the time. Add the pasta, Quorn, mustard and cheese, and bring to the boil stirring continuously.

Spoon the leek and Quorn mixture into an ovenproof dish. Arrange the tomatoes over the mixture. Bake in the pre-heated oven for 25 minutes.

Tip:

Quorn is a meat substitute. It has been developed from a fungus and contains protein, dietary fibre and fat, however, none of the fat is of animal origin.

1 tbs oil
1 large clove garlic, finely
    chopped
1 large onion, chopped
2 sticks celery, chopped
4 oz (120 g) carrot, chopped
4 oz (120 g) green lentils
4 oz (120 g) split red lentils
1 tbs tomato purée
15 oz (450 g) canned chopped
    tomatoes
4 fl oz (120 ml) dry white wine
12 fl oz (360 ml) vegetable stock
¼ tsp cinnamon
¼ tsp dried basil
6 oz (180 g) spaghetti

Lentil Bolognaise

SERVES 4

PREPARATION AND COOKING TIME: 45 MINUTES

Heat the oil in a large saucepan and stir-fry the garlic and onion for 3 minutes, add the celery and carrot and stir-fry for a further 3 minutes. Stir in the lentils, tomato purée, chopped tomatoes, wine, stock, cinnamon and basil. Bring to the boil, stir well then reduce the heat, cover and cook gently for 30 minutes.

About 10 minutes before the end of the lentils' cooking time, boil a large saucepan of water, add the spaghetti and a little salt and cook for about 10 minutes or according to the packaging instructions.

Drain the spaghetti and divide between four warm serving plates.

salt and pepper
1 oz (30 g) Parmesan or mature
    Cheddar cheese, finely grated

SELECTIONS PER SERVING:

1½ Bread
½ Fat
2 Protein
2¼ Vegetable
50 Optional Calories

CALORIES PER
SERVING: 440

Season the Bolognaise with salt and pepper and spoon on top of each serving of spaghetti. Sprinkle over the cheese and serve.

Tip:

Always add salt after cooking pulses otherwise it may toughen their skins and will drastically increase the cooking time.

1 clove garlic, finely chopped
1 onion, sliced
1 carrot, sliced
3 oz (90 g) green beans, sliced
4 oz (120 g) fennel, chopped
2 oz (60 g) frozen peas
15 oz (450 g) canned chopped
    tomatoes
½ tsp dried basil
1 lb (480 g) skinned smoked cod
    fillet
2 tbs cornflour
2 tbs water or stock
For the crumble:
1 oz (30 g) wholemeal flour
1½ oz (45 g) white flour
1½ oz (45 g) margarine
1½ oz (45 g) mature Cheddar
    cheese, finely grated

SELECTIONS PER SERVING:

½ Bread
2 Fat
2 Protein
2½ Vegetable
45 Optional Calories

CALORIES PER
SERVING: 350

Smoked Cod Crumble

SERVES 4

PREPARATION AND COOKING TIME: 50 MINUTES

Pre-heat the oven to 180°C, 350°F, Gas Mark 4.

Place all the vegetables and basil in a large saucepan. Bring to the boil over a moderate heat, cover and simmer for 12 minutes.

Cut the fish, across the fillet, into 1½ inch (4 cm) strips.

Blend the cornflour to a paste with the water or stock, set aside while preparing the crumble.

Mix the flours together in a mixing bowl, rub in the margarine (if possible margarine which has been stored in the freezer) with your fingertips until the mixture resembles fresh breadcrumbs. Stir in the cheese.

Stir the blended cornflour into the boiling vegetables. Return to the boil, stirring all the time. Boil for 1–2 minutes then reduce the heat, add the fish and stir over a low heat for 3–4 minutes.

Spoon the fish and vegetables into a deep ovenproof dish, sprinkle over the crumble and bake in the pre-heated oven for 25 minutes.

Tip:

You can make double the amount of crumble topping then freeze half to use as a topping over a meat or vegetable base.

Fish Stew

2 tsps oil
1 or 2 cloves garlic, finely
    chopped
1 large onion, roughly chopped
3 oz (90 g) fennel, sliced
4 oz (120 g) carrots, cut into
    ½ inch (1.25 cm) cubes
1 tbs tomato purée
6 fl oz (180 ml) stock
15 oz (450 g) canned chopped
    tomatoes
1 lb (480 g) potatoes, cut into
    1–1½ inch (2.5–4 cm)
    chunks
2 oz (60 g) okra
8 oz (240 g) courgettes, thickly
    sliced
1 lb 2 oz (540 g) mixture of
    skinned and boned firm-
    fleshed white fish, e.g. red
    mullet, monkfish; cut into
    2 inch (5 cm) pieces
salt and pepper

SELECTIONS PER SERVING:

1 Bread
½ Fat
2 Protein
3¼ Vegetable

CALORIES PER
SERVING: 265

SERVES 4
PREPARATION AND COOKING TIME: 50 MINUTES

Heat the oil in a large saucepan and stir-fry the garlic and onion for 2 minutes. Add the fennel, carrots, tomato purée and stock, stir well then cover the saucepan and cook gently over a low heat for 10 minutes.

Add the chopped tomatoes, potatoes and okra to the saucepan and bring to the boil. Stir, cover and leave to simmer gently for 10 minutes. Finally, add the courgettes, bring to the boil for 1–2 minutes, then reduce the heat and add the fish. Stir gently, cover the saucepan and simmer for 10–14 minutes or until the fish is cooked. Season with salt and pepper to taste and serve.

Tip:

The stew may be frozen but take care not to overcook the fish or it will lose its texture when reheated.

Variation:

Add a few mussels or prawns to the stew if desired but remember to add the additional Selections.

Right: Fish Stew

Feta Cheese and Broccoli Savoury Roll

For the roll:
1 oz (30 g) margarine
1 oz (30 g) flour
8 fl oz (240 ml) skimmed milk
2 eggs, separated
salt
For the filling:
6 oz (180 g) broccoli, divided into florets
salt
1 tbs margarine
1 oz (30 g) flour
4 fl oz (120 ml) skimmed milk
3 oz (90 g) feta cheese
pepper
lemon juice

SELECTIONS PER SERVING:

½ Bread
2 Fat
¼ Milk
1 Protein
½ Vegetable
30 Optional Calories

CALORIES PER
SERVING: 255

SERVES 4

PREPARATION AND COOKING TIME: 55 MINUTES

Pre-heat the oven to 180°C, 350°F, Gas Mark 4.

Line an 11 × 7 inch (27.5 × 17.5 cm) Swiss-roll tin with non-stick baking parchment.

Prepare the roll. Melt the margarine in a saucepan, add the flour and cook for 1–2 minutes, stirring all the time. Gradually blend in the milk and bring to the boil stirring continuously, boil for 2 minutes. Stir in the egg yolks.

Place the egg whites in a clean bowl, add a pinch of salt and whisk until peaking. Using a metal spoon carefully fold the whisked egg whites into the sauce.

Spoon the mixture evenly all over the lined tin, and spread carefully taking care not to mix it too much. Level the surface and bake in the pre-heated oven for 30–35 minutes until golden.

While the roll is cooking prepare the filling. Boil the broccoli in lightly salted water until just cooked, do not overcook.

Melt the margarine in a saucepan, add the flour and mix as evenly as possible. Gradually blend in the milk.

Drain the broccoli well and transfer to a liquidiser, add the blended flour and milk and process to a purée. Pour the purée into the saucepan and bring to the boil, stirring all the time. Boil for about 3 minutes until thick. Crumble in the feta cheese and remove from the heat. Adjust the seasoning to taste, adding salt, pepper and lemon juice as desired.

Turn the cooked roll out on to a sheet of non-stick baking parchment lying flat on an even work surface. Carefully strip off the lining paper. Spread the broccoli sauce over the cooked roll, leaving a clear edge about 1–1½ inch (2.5–4 cm) along both long sides and one of the short sides. Using the paper for support, loosely roll up from the short side covered with the filling to the short side with the clear edge. Cut the roll into four pieces with a sharp knife then, using a fish slice, transfer to four warm serving plates and serve immediately.

Variation:

This roll may be served cold – turn the cooked roll out on to a sheet of non-stick baking parchment, lay another piece of parchment on top and roll up and leave until cold. When cold unroll, spread with the cold broccoli sauce and re-roll. Do not spread the hot roll with the sauce then leave to cool as the filling will ooze out.

Chicken Casserole with Tarragon Dumplings

SERVES 4
PREPARATION AND COOKING TIME: 2 HOURS 15 MINUTES

2 tsps oil
13 oz (390 g) boned and skinned chicken or turkey thighs, cut into 2 inch (5 cm) pieces
4 oz (120 g) carrots, sliced
6 oz (180 g) leeks, thickly sliced
2 oz (60 g) fennel, sliced
3 oz (90 g) mushrooms, sliced
8 oz (240 g) canned chopped tomatoes
½ pint (300 ml) vegetable or chicken stock
1 oz (30 g) cooked ham, cut into ½ inch (1.25 cm) strips
2 tsps vegetable purée
For the dumplings:
4 oz (120 g) self-raising flour
½ oz (15 g) fresh breadcrumbs
2½ tbs margarine
¼ tsp dried tarragon
salt and pepper
¼ pint (150 ml) water

SELECTIONS PER SERVING:

1 Bread
2 Fat
3 Protein
2 Vegetable
25 Optional Calories

CALORIES PER
SERVING: 350

Pre-heat the oven to 160°C, 325°F, Gas Mark 3.

Heat the oil in a flameproof casserole, add the chicken or turkey and stir-fry over a high heat for 2 minutes until it has lost its pink colour and begun to brown. Add the prepared vegetables, chopped tomatoes, stock, ham and vegetable purée to the casserole and bring to the boil, stir well and cover. Cook in the pre-heated oven for 1 hour 40 minutes.

Shortly before the end of the cooking time make the dumplings. Mix the flour and breadcrumbs together in a bowl and rub the margarine (if possible margarine which has been stored in the freezer) into the flour mixture with your fingertips. Add the tarragon and a sprinkling of salt and pepper. Mix with cold water to form a soft dough. Form into eight balls.

Arrange the dumplings on top of the casserole, cover and return to the oven. Cook for a further 20 minutes until the dumplings are cooked.

Tip:

This recipe is best frozen without the dumplings then when thawed reheat the Chicken Casserole, make the dumplings and cook as described above.

Illustrated on pages 118/119

2 tbs oil
2 large onions, sliced
1 large green pepper, deseeded
    and cut into strips
2 tbs paprika
½ tbs flour
2 × 250 g packets Quorn
1 tbs tomato purée
15 oz (450 g) canned chopped
    tomatoes
½ pint (300 ml) lager
6 oz (180 g) baby corn on the
    cob
salt

SELECTIONS PER SERVING:

½ Bread
1½ Fat
2 Protein
2 Vegetable
30 Optional Calories

CALORIES PER
SERVING: 280

Paprika Quorn with Tomatoes and Baby Corn

SERVES 4

PREPARATION AND COOKING TIME: 45 MINUTES

Heat the oil in a large saucepan and stir-fry the onions and green pepper until the onions are soft. Sprinkle in the paprika and flour and stir well, add all the remaining ingredients. Bring to the boil stirring all the time.

Reduce the heat and simmer for 30–35 minutes.

Variation:

To make a filling meal serve this recipe with 3 oz (90 g) cooked rice or pasta per person and add 1 Bread Selection. Calories per serving will be 360.

---

1 lb 12 oz (840 g) potatoes,
    peeled and sliced
salt
3 tbs margarine
4 tbs finely grated Parmesan
    cheese
pepper

SELECTIONS PER SERVING:

1 Bread
1½ Fat
35 Optional Calories

CALORIES PER
SERVING: 190

Crispy Potatoes

SERVES 6

PREPARATION AND COOKING TIME: 30 MINUTES

Boil the potatoes in salted water until cooked, drain.

Grease a deep flameproof dish, about 8–9 inch (20–22.5 cm) in diameter, with a little of the margarine. Arrange one-third of the hot drained potatoes in the dish and sprinkle over half the cheese. Season with salt and pepper. Continue with another layer of potatoes, top with the remaining cheese and lastly the rest of the potatoes, seasoning each layer with salt and pepper.

Dot the margarine over the potatoes and cook under a hot grill for 4–5 minutes until golden brown.

Shepherd's Pie

14 oz (420 g) minced beef or
  lamb
2 tsps oil
1 onion, chopped
6 oz (180 g) carrot, diced
1½ tbs flour
15 oz (450 g) canned chopped
  tomatoes
1 tsp dried basil
½ tsp dried marjoram
salt and pepper
1 lb 8 oz (720 g) potatoes,
  peeled
2 tbs skimmed milk
2 tsps margarine

SELECTIONS PER SERVING:

1½ Bread
1 Fat
3 Protein
2½ Vegetable
15 Optional Calories

CALORIES PER
SERVING: 385

SERVES 4
PREPARATION AND COOKING TIME: 50 MINUTES

Form the minced meat into four patties, place on the rack of a grill pan and cook under a low heat, turning once, until the fat stops dripping from the meat.

Heat the oil in a large saucepan and stir-fry the onion for 4 minutes. Add the carrot and stir over a moderate heat for 2 minutes. Sprinkle in the flour, stir well then mix in the tomatoes and herbs. Crumble the meat patties into the saucepan and add a little salt and pepper. Bring to the boil, stir then cover and cook gently over a low heat for 25 minutes.

While the meat is cooking boil the potatoes in slightly salted water until cooked. Drain then mash together with the milk and margarine.

Spoon the cooked minced meat and vegetables into a flameproof dish, top with the mashed potatoes and roughen the surface with a fork. Brown under a pre-heated hot grill.

Variation:

Sprinkle 1 oz (30 g) grated cheese over the potato before grilling – remember to add 15 Optional Calories to every serving (415 Calories per serving).

Illustrated on pages 118/119

Apple Pudding

For the apple base:
1 lb 4 oz (600 g) cooking apples, peeled, cored and cut into thick slices
3 oz (90 g) raisins
juice of ½ medium orange
artificial sweetener
For the topping:
2 oz (60 g) self-raising flour
1 oz (30 g) caster sugar
2 eggs, separated
finely grated zest of 1 orange
¼ pint (150 ml) skimmed milk
pinch of salt

SELECTIONS PER SERVING:

½ Bread
2 Fruit
½ Protein
50 Optional Calories

CALORIES PER
SERVING: 240

SERVES 4
PREPARATION AND COOKING TIME: 55 MINUTES

Pre-heat the oven to 190°C, 375°F, Gas Mark 5.

Place the apples in a saucepan with the raisins and orange juice, cover and cook gently over a low to moderate heat for 8–10 minutes while preparing the topping.

In a large bowl mix together the flour with the sugar, make a well in the centre and place the egg yolks in the well. Add the orange zest and using a wooden spoon gradually mix in the milk to form a smooth batter.

Place the egg whites in a clean bowl, add a pinch of salt and whisk until peaking. Gradually fold the egg whites into the batter.

Sweeten the apples with artificial sweetener and spoon into a deep soufflé dish. Spoon over the topping and bake in the pre-heated oven for 30 minutes until well-risen and golden brown. Serve immediately.

Variation:

Add a pinch of cloves to the apples and use wholemeal self-raising flour for the topping – it gives a slightly nutty flavour.

Vanilla Custard

1 egg
1 egg yolk
1 tsp cornflour
1 tbs caster sugar
½ pint (300 ml) skimmed milk
few drops of vanilla essence

SELECTIONS PER SERVING:

¼ Milk
45 Optional Calories

CALORIES PER
SERVING: 85

SERVES 4
PREPARATION AND COOKING TIME: 15 MINUTES

Beat together the whole egg with the egg yolk, cornflour, caster sugar and 2 tablespoons milk.

Heat the remaining milk until beginning to steam. Pour the hot milk into the egg mixture, stirring all the time.

Strain the custard into a clean saucepan, add the vanilla essence and cook gently over a very low heat, stirring constantly, until the custard thickens and coats the back of a spoon. Do not allow to boil or the custard will separate.

Variation:

For a creamier taste substitute the skimmed milk with whole milk. Selections will be ¼ Milk and 70 Optional Calories. (Total Calories per serving 105.)

Apple and Plum Filled Pancakes

SERVES 4

PREPARATION AND COOKING TIME: 35 MINUTES

For the filling:

8 medium plums, halved, stoned and cut into wedges

8 oz (240 g) cooking apples, peeled, cored and thinly sliced

2 tbs water

1½ oz (45 g) sugar

1½ tsps arrowroot or cornflour

For the pancakes:

4 oz (120 g) plain flour

pinch of salt

1 egg

½ pint (300 ml) skimmed milk

4 tsps oil

SELECTIONS PER SERVING:

1 Bread
1 Fat
1½ Fruit
¼ Milk
65 Optional Calories

CALORIES PER
SERVING: 290

Prepare the filling. Place the fruit in a saucepan, add the water and sprinkle in the sugar. Cover the saucepan and cook gently over a very low heat for 10–12 minutes until the fruit is cooked but still whole. Blend the arrowroot or cornflour with a little cold water and set aside.

While the fruit is cooking prepare and make the pancakes. Sift the flour and salt into a mixing bowl, make a well in the centre and break the egg into it. Gradually beat or whisk in the milk.

Prove a 7 inch (17.5 cm) frying pan by generously sprinkling salt over the base and heating gently, tipping out the salt and wiping the pan thoroughly with kitchen paper. This will help prevent the pancakes sticking. Heat a little oil in the frying pan and wipe again with the kitchen paper.

Heat a little more oil in the frying pan and pour in some batter at the same time turning the pan so it thinly coats the base. Cook over a moderate heat until the underside is golden brown then toss or turn over and cook the other side.

Transfer the cooked pancake to a plate; cover and keep warm while repeating the procedure to make 12 pancakes.

Drain the fruit and place in a bowl. Stir the blended arrowroot or cornflour into the hot fruit juices and bring to the boil, boil for 1 minute stirring all the time.

Spoon a little fruit and some of the thickened sauce into each pancake, fold into quarters. Arrange on a warm serving plate.

Tip:

The pancakes may be made in advance and interleaved with foil then frozen. Cook the fruit and freeze separately in an airtight container leaving ½ inch (1.25 cm) headspace.

Steamed Sponge Pudding

1 tsp margarine
5 oz (150 g) plain flour
1 oz (30 g) caster sugar
finely grated zest of ½ a lemon
2 eggs, separated
¼ pint (150 ml) skimmed milk
2 oz (60 g) currants, sultanas or
    mixture of dried fruit
pinch of cream of tartar

SELECTIONS PER SERVING:

1 Bread
½ Fruit
½ Protein
70 Optional Calories

CALORIES PER
SERVING: 255

SERVES 4
PREPARATION AND COOKING TIME: 1 HOUR 40 MINUTES

Grease a 1½ pint (900 ml) pudding basin with the margarine.

Sieve the flour into a mixing bowl, stir in the sugar and lemon zest. Add the egg yolks and milk and gradually beat into the flour. Stir in the dried fruit.

In a clean bowl whisk the egg whites with the cream of tartar until peaking. Using a metal spoon fold into the flour mixture. Spoon into the prepared basin.

Cover the top of the basin with a large piece of pleated non-stick baking parchment, secure it by tying a piece of string around the rim. Steam for 1 hour 30 minutes.

To serve: turn the pudding out of the basin and serve immediately with a custard or white sauce.

Tip:

The pudding must be served immediately as it will sink as it cools. It is not suitable for freezing.

Steamed Sponge Pudding

Jamaican Crumble

For the crumble topping:

**2½ oz (75 g) white or
  wholemeal flour**

1½ oz (45 g) margarine

½ oz (15 g) porridge oats

good pinch of ground ginger

2 tsps soft brown sugar

4 tsps desiccated coconut

For the base:

juice of ½ a lemon

4 tsps soft brown sugar

6 tbs water

**8 oz (240 g) fresh pineapple, cut
  into 1 inch (2.5 cm) cubes**

**6 lychees, peeled, halved and
  stoned**

4 fresh dates, halved and stoned

½ medium banana, sliced

SELECTIONS PER SERVING:

½ Bread
2 Fat
1½ Fruit
70 Optional Calories

CALORIES PER
SERVING: 265

SERVES 4

PREPARATION AND COOKING TIME: 50 MINUTES

Pre-heat the oven to 180°C, 350°F, Gas Mark 4.

First of all make the crumble. Place the flour in a mixing bowl and rub in the margarine (if possible margarine which has been stored in the freezer) with your fingertips until the mixture resembles fresh breadcrumbs. Stir in the porridge oats, ginger, sugar and coconut.

To make the base, pour the lemon juice into a small saucepan, add the sugar and water and heat gently until the sugar has dissolved.

Mix all the prepared fruit together in a deep 5 inch (12.5 cm) ovenproof dish, pour over the syrup and sprinkle the crumble topping evenly over the fruit.

Bake in the pre-heated oven for 35 minutes.

Tip:

Brush a little lemon juice over the cut surface of the remaining banana and use the following day – do not refrigerate or it will turn black.

Jamaican Crumble

1 lb (480 g) rhubarb, cut into
   1½ inch (4 cm) lengths
1 lb (480 g) cooking apples,
   peeled, cored and cut into
   chunks
1 tbs water
artificial sweetener
2 tsps flour
3 oz (90 g) ready-made
   shortcrust pastry (see Chicken
   and Vegetable Pie on page
   125)

SELECTIONS PER SERVING:

½ Bread
1½ Fat
1 Fruit
5 Optional Calories

CALORIES PER
SERVING: 150

Rhubarb and Apple Lattice

SERVES 4

PREPARATION AND COOKING TIME: 45 MINUTES

Pre-heat the oven to 220°C, 425°F, Gas Mark 7.

Put the rhubarb and apple in a saucepan, add the water, cover and cook gently over a low heat for about 12 minutes, stirring occasionally. The fruit should be just cooked with its shape and some texture retained. Sweeten to taste with artificial sweetener. Spoon the fruit into a pie dish.

Dust the work surface and a rolling pin with the flour and roll out the pastry until about ¼ inch (5 mm) thick, cut into ½ inch (1.25 cm) strips. Arrange the strips in a lattice pattern over the fruit. Bake in the pre-heated oven for 15–20 minutes until the pastry is light golden brown.

Tip:

This pastry may be made by following the basic recipe for shortcrust pastry in the Chicken and Vegetable Pie recipe (page 125). The quantity required will be 2 oz (60 g) flour and 1 oz (30 g) margarine mixed with 2 teaspoons ice-cold water.

2 tbs margarine
½ pint (300 ml) skimmed milk
6 oz (180 g) wholemeal bread
2 oz (60 g) dried stoned dates,
   chopped
2 oz (60 g) ready-to-eat dried
   apricots, chopped
1½ oz (45 g) raisins
1½ oz (45 g) sultanas
finely grated zest of ½–1 lemon
¼ tsp mixed spice
1 egg
1 medium dessert apple, peeled,
   cored and diced
2 tbs desiccated coconut
½ tsp caster sugar

Bread and Fruit Pudding

SERVES 4

PREPARATION AND COOKING TIME: 1 HOUR 15 MINUTES

PLUS 30 MINUTES SOAKING

Pre-heat the oven to 180°C, 350°F, Gas Mark 4.

Grease a 1½ pint (900 ml) pie dish with a little of the margarine. Place the remainder in a saucepan with the milk and heat gently until steaming.

Break the bread into pieces and process in a liquidiser or food processor to form breadcrumbs.

Place the dates and apricots in a bowl together with the breadcrumbs, raisins, sultanas, lemon zest and spice. Pour in the steaming milk and margarine, stir well and set aside for 30 minutes.

SELECTIONS PER SERVING:

1½ Bread
1½ Fat
2 Fruit
¼ Milk
30 Optional Calories

CALORIES PER
SERVING: 345

Lightly beat the egg. Stir the soaked bread and fruit then mix in the egg, apple and coconut. Spoon into the greased pie dish and bake in the pre-heated oven for 1 hour. Sprinkle with the caster sugar and serve.

Variation:

This pudding is delicious served with fromage frais or low fat natural yogurt, but remember to add the extra Selections.

1½ lb (720 g) plums, halved and stoned
3 tbs apple juice
artificial sweetener
For the crumble topping:
3 oz (90 g) flour
1½ oz (45 g) margarine
1 tbs caster sugar

SELECTIONS PER SERVING:

½ Bread
2 Fat
1½ Fruit
50 Optional Calories

CALORIES PER
SERVING: 240

Plum Crumble

SERVES 4
PREPARATION AND COOKING TIME: 40 MINUTES

Pre-heat the oven to 190°C, 375°F, Gas Mark 5.

Place the plums in a saucepan with the apple juice and simmer gently over a low heat until the plums are half cooked. Sweeten the fruit with a little artificial sweetener and place in a small deep ovenproof dish – if the plums have produced a great deal of juice reserve some to reheat and serve with the crumble.

Place the flour in a mixing bowl, add the margarine (if possible margarine which has been stored in the freezer) and rub in with your fingertips until the mixture resembles fresh breadcrumbs.

Spoon the crumble topping over the plums, sprinkle over the sugar and bake in the pre-heated oven for 20–25 minutes.

Variation:

If you prefer, use 1 lb (480 g) damsons and ½ lb (240 g) apples. The Selections will remain the same.

Plum Crumble *illustrated overleaf*

8 tsps margarine
3 medium oranges
8 oz (240 g) self-raising flour
¼ tsp baking powder
3 oz (90 g) caster sugar
3 oz (90 g) dried stoned dates,
    finely chopped
1 egg
7 fl oz (210 ml) skimmed milk
1½ tbs arrowroot
½–1 tsp lemon juice

SELECTIONS PER SERVING:

1 Bread
1 Fat
½ Fruit
80 Optional Calories

CALORIES PER
SERVING: 245

Orange and Date Puddings

SERVES 8

PREPARATION AND COOKING TIME: 45 MINUTES

Pre-heat the oven to 180°C, 350°F, Gas Mark 4.

Use 1–2 teaspoons margarine to grease the sides of eight ramekins. Line the bases with circles of non-stick baking parchment.

Finely grate the zest of two oranges, place the zest of one in a small saucepan and the other in a mixing bowl. Sieve the flour and baking powder into the bowl with the orange zest, rub in the remaining margarine with your fingertips. Stir in 2½ oz (75 g) of the sugar and the dates, breaking up any lumps of dates which stick together.

Beat the egg and milk together, using a metal spoon, stir into the date and flour mixture. Mix well and spoon into the ramekins.

Bake in the pre-heated oven for 25–30 minutes. The time depends on the thickness of the ramekin so check each pudding is cooked by inserting a skewer in the centre, if it comes out clean it is cooked, if not continue cooking then retest. Leave the puddings for 2 minutes, turn out of the ramekins then turn right side up and place on individual serving plates.

While the puddings are cooking make the orange sauce: squeeze the juice from the oranges and pour into a measuring jug, make up to 12 fl oz (360 ml) with water. Blend a little of the orange and water into the arrowroot, bring the remainder to the boil in the saucepan with the orange zest. Gradually stir the boiling liquid into the arrowroot, return to the saucepan and boil for 1 minute, stirring all the time. Stir in the remaining sugar and lemon juice. Adjust the flavouring to suit your taste, if you have a particularly sweet tooth add a little artificial sweetener.

Pierce the top of each pudding five or six times with a skewer then slowly pour over the orange sauce so it seeps into the pudding and runs down the sides.

Tip:

Cornflour may be used in place of the arrowroot but the sauce will not have the opaque orange colour.

Orange and Date Puddings *illustrated on previous page*

Apricot and Almond Batter Pudding

4 oz (120 g) plain flour

pinch of salt

1 egg

½ pint (300 ml) skimmed milk

¼ tsp almond essence

1 tbs caster sugar

1 tsp margarine

8 oz (240 g) well-drained canned apricot halves

½ oz (15 g) almond kernels, roughly chopped

½ tsp icing sugar

SELECTIONS PER SERVING:

1 Bread
½ Fruit
¼ Milk
½ Protein
30 Optional Calories

CALORIES PER
SERVING: 215

SERVES 4

PREPARATION AND COOKING TIME: 1 HOUR 10 MINUTES

Pre-heat the oven to 220°C, 425°F, Gas Mark 7.

Sieve the flour and salt into a mixing bowl. Make a well in the centre and break the egg into it. Add a little of the milk and gradually mix together with a wooden spoon drawing the flour from the outside towards the centre. Gradually mix in all the milk to make a smooth batter. Stir in the almond essence and caster sugar and set aside.

Grease an ovenproof dish, about 9 × 12 inch (22.5 × 30 cm) with the margarine.

Dab the apricots with kitchen paper so they are as dry as possible. Either leave the apricots as halves or roughly chop and dab once again with the kitchen paper.

Sprinkle the almonds into the greased dish and arrange the apricots evenly on top. Cook in the pre-heated oven for 8 or 9 minutes until very hot.

Stir the batter and pour over the apricots – take care not to move all the apricots to one end of the dish. Return the pudding to the oven and cook at the same temperature for about 45 minutes until well-risen, golden brown and puffy. If the batter between the apricot pieces is not golden continue cooking for a few more minutes. Remove from the oven, sprinkle over the icing sugar and serve immediately.

Tip:

Do not open the oven door until the pudding has been in the oven for at least 30 minutes.

It's so Simple!

How many times have you not attempted a recipe because it looks too difficult to make? Whether you wish to eat more nutritious meals or want to lose weight, your diet should always be varied and interesting. To help you achieve this goal all the recipes in the MADE TO MEASURE COOK BOOK use a wide variety of nutritious ingredients, which are delicious to eat and all are based on the Weight Watchers Programme. Some recipes do sound difficult to make, but if you follow the method closely and start with a recipe that uses few ingredients, for example Carrot and Orange Soup (page 159), you will soon gain confidence and be able to create more complicated meals.

For example, very few people bake their own bread because they think it is too difficult and time-consuming. The 'Short Time' Wholemeal Bread (page 176), however, includes a vitamin C tablet in the ingredients which eliminates one of the rising stages. Likewise soufflés are frequently not made because they collapse so quickly when they are removed from the oven. The recipe for Cheese Soufflé (page page 165) is divided into clear stages of preparation and as long as you keep to the golden rule that the guests must wait for the soufflé not the soufflé for the guests, you will be able to serve it quickly while it is still risen!

4 oz (120 g) soft blue cheese,
   e.g. blue Brie; rind removed
2 tsps margarine
2 medium onions, chopped
¾ pint (450 ml) vegetable or
   chicken stock
12 oz (360 g) potatoes, diced
2 oz (60 g) watercress, roughly
   chopped
1½ inch (4 cm) strip of lemon
   zest
salt and pepper
2 oz (60 g) dried skimmed milk

SELECTIONS PER SERVING:

½ Bread
½ Fat
½ Milk
1 Protein
½ Vegetable
20 Optional Calories

CALORIES PER
SERVING: 265

Potato and Watercress Soup with Blue Cheese

SERVES 4
PREPARATION AND COOKING TIME: 40 MINUTES

Place the blue cheese in the freezer while preparing and cooking the vegetables.

Heat the margarine in a saucepan, add the onions and stir round then cover the saucepan and cook over a low heat for 6–7 minutes. Stir in the stock, potatoes, watercress and lemon zest. Season well, cover and simmer gently for about 25 minutes.

While the soup is cooking mix the dried milk with 3 tablespoons water. Cut the cheese into ¼ inch (5 mm) dice then return it to the freezer.

Pour the watercress mixture into a liquidiser and process to a smooth purée. Pour the purée into a saucepan and stir in the milk. Bring to the boil stirring all the time. Adjust the seasoning, adding more salt and pepper as necessary.

Stir the diced cheese into the boiling soup, ladle into warm soup bowls and serve immediately.

2 tsps oil
1 onion, finely chopped
1 large clove garlic, crushed
¼ tsp yeast extract
4 oz (120 g) canned chestnut
   purée
1 oz (30 g) curd cheese
1½ tbs Madeira wine
1 oz (30 g) mixed nuts, finely
   chopped
salt and pepper

SELECTIONS PER SERVING:

½ Fat
½ Protein
¼ Vegetable
55 Optional Calories

CALORIES PER
SERVING: 130

Cheesy Chestnut Pâté

SERVES 4
PREPARATION AND COOKING TIME: 15 MINUTES PLUS CHILLING

Heat the oil in a small saucepan and stir-fry the onion for 1–2 minutes then cover the pan and leave to steam over a very low heat for 3 minutes or until soft. Stir the garlic together with the cooked onion and yeast extract.

Blend in the chestnut purée and curd cheese then stir in the Madeira wine. Finally stir the nuts into the pâté and season well with salt and pepper. Spoon into a small bowl and chill.

Tip:

There is no need to remove the skins from the nut kernels, unblanched almonds are more economical than blanched. Serve the pâté spread on 1 oz (30 g) thin slices of toast or crusty bread per serving, add 1 Bread Selection and increase Total Calories per serving to 195.

Tuna and Chive Pâté

4 oz (120 g) well-drained
    canned tuna
2 oz (60 g) curd cheese
2 tsps chopped fresh chives
4 tsps mayonnaise
4 tsps lemon juice
1 tsp chopped capers
salt and pepper

SELECTIONS PER SERVING:

1 Fat
½ Protein
15 Optional Calories

CALORIES PER
SERVING: 80

SERVES 4

PREPARATION: 10 MINUTES

NO COOKING REQUIRED

Mash the tuna with a fork in a small bowl. Add the curd cheese and mix with the tuna until evenly combined. Blend in the chives, mayonnaise, lemon juice and capers and mix well.

Season to taste with salt and pepper and add a little more lemon juice if desired. Serve as a spread on toast or use as a filling for rolls.

Tip:

If the pâté is too stiff to spread on bread to make sandwiches, add a little milk or low fat natural yogurt and mix well. Add the additional Optional Calories as necessary.

Stilton and Walnut Pâté

2 oz (60 g) Stilton cheese
1½ oz (45 g) curd cheese
1 tbs port wine
1 tbs low fat natural yogurt
¼ oz (10 g) walnut kernels,
    chopped

SELECTIONS PER SERVING:

½ Protein
30 Optional Calories

CALORIES PER
SERVING: 95

SERVES 4

PREPARATION: 5 MINUTES

NO COOKING REQUIRED

Crumble the Stilton cheese into a small bowl. Using a fork gradually mash the curd cheese together with the Stilton. Mix in the port wine and then the yogurt.

Reserve about 1 teaspoon of the walnuts and stir the remainder into the cheese mixture.

Spoon the pâté into a ramekin, smooth the top then sprinkle over the reserved walnuts. Refrigerate until ready to serve.

Tip:

Serve with 1 oz (30 g) hot toast per serving or use as a tasty sandwich spread. Add 1 Bread Selection and increase Total Calories per serving to 160. Freezing is not recommended.

Tuna and Chive and Stilton and Walnut Patés *illustrated overleaf*

Carrot and Orange Soup

1 large leek, thinly sliced
1 lb 4 oz (600 g) carrots, sliced
1¼ pints (750 ml) vegetable or
    chicken stock
good pinch of dried thyme
juice of 1 medium orange
salt and pepper

SELECTIONS PER SERVING:

2½ Vegetable
15 Optional Calories

CALORIES PER
SERVING: 50

SERVES 4

PREPARATION AND COOKING TIME: 45 MINUTES

Place the leek (reserving two or three slices), carrots, stock and thyme in a saucepan and bring to the boil, reduce the heat, cover and simmer for 30 minutes until the vegetables are cooked.

Process the vegetables and stock in a liquidiser or food processor until smooth. Pour the purée back into the saucepan and stir in the orange juice.

Plunge the reserved slices of leek into boiling water and boil for 1–2 minutes.

Bring the soup to the boil, season with salt and pepper and ladle into warm soup bowls. Scatter the slices of leek over each serving of soup.

Left: Tuna and Chive Paté (top), Stilton and Walnut Paté (bottom)

Right: Carrot and Orange Soup

6–7 oz (180–210 g) aubergine,
    cut into 1 inch (2.5 cm) cubes
salt
1 tsp oil
1 clove garlic, finely chopped
1 large onion, roughly chopped
1 large red pepper, deseeded
    and roughly chopped
2 sticks celery, sliced
15 oz (450 g) canned chopped
    tomatoes
1 tbs tomato purée
2 tsps chopped fresh basil
6 oz (180 g) potato, cut into ¾
    inch (2 cm) cubes
6 oz (180 g) courgettes, thickly
    sliced
2½ tbs margarine
1½ oz (45 g) flour
¾ pint (450 ml) skimmed milk
4 oz (120 g) feta cheese, grated
1 large egg, separated

SELECTIONS PER SERVING:

½ Bread
2 Fat
¼ Milk
1 Protein
3 Vegetable
50 Optional Calories

CALORIES PER
SERVING: 300

Vegetable Bake with Feta Cheese Sauce

SERVES 4

PREPARATION AND COOKING TIME: 1 HOUR 20 MINUTES

Pre-heat the oven to 180°C, 350°F, Gas Mark 4.

Place the aubergine in a sieve or colander and sprinkle liberally with salt.

Heat the oil in a saucepan, add the garlic, onion, red pepper and celery and stir-fry for 5 minutes then add the chopped tomatoes, tomato purée, basil and potato. Bring the vegetables to the boil, stir well, cover the saucepan and leave to simmer over a low heat for 15 minutes.

Rinse the aubergine well under running cold water, pat dry. Add the courgettes and aubergine to the simmering vegetables, cover the saucepan and continue simmering for 5 minutes. Stir well and simmer uncovered for about 5–6 minutes while preparing the sauce.

Melt the margarine in a small saucepan, add the flour and stir well. Remove from the heat and gradually blend in the milk. Bring to the boil, stirring all the time, boil for 2 minutes. Reserve about ½ oz (15 g) of the feta cheese and add the remainder to the sauce, stir well. Blend in the egg yolk.

Place the egg white in a clean bowl, add a pinch of salt and whisk until peaking. Using a metal spoon fold the egg white into the cheese sauce.

Spoon the vegetables into a large ovenproof dish, pour the sauce over and sprinkle with the reserved cheese. Bake in the pre-heated oven for 40–45 minutes. Serve immediately.

Tip:

The vegetable base of this bake may be prepared in advance and refrigerated overnight or frozen. The sauce must be made just before baking.

Couscous with Spicy Vegetables

8 oz (240 g) couscous
4 tsps oil
2 cloves garlic, finely chopped
½ tbs ground cumin
½ tbs ground coriander
1 tsp turmeric
2 onions, chopped
1 red pepper, deseeded and cut
    into ½ inch (1.25 cm)
    squares
1 green pepper, deseeded and
    cut into ½ inch (1.25 cm)
    squares
8 oz (240 g) courgette, cut into
    ½ inch (1.25 cm) cubes
4 oz (120 g) parsnip, cut into
    ½ inch (1.25 cm) cubes
2 carrots, cut into ½ inch
    (1.25 cm) cubes
6 oz (180 g) drained canned
    chick peas
15 oz (450 g) canned chopped
    tomatoes
2 oz (60 g) raisins
12 fl oz (360 ml) water or
    vegetable stock

SELECTIONS PER SERVING:

2 Bread
1 Fat
½ Fruit
½ Protein
3 Vegetable
20 Optional Calories

CALORIES PER
SERVING: 350

SERVES 4

PREPARATION AND COOKING TIME: 1 HOUR

Prepare the couscous as described on the packaging instructions.

Heat the oil in a large saucepan and stir-fry the garlic for 1–2 minutes. Add the cumin, coriander, turmeric and all the prepared vegetables and stir-fry for 2–3 minutes then cover, reduce the heat and leave to steam for 8–9 minutes. Mix the chick peas, tomatoes, raisins and water or stock into the vegetables and bring to the boil.

Spoon the couscous into a metal sieve or steamer. Stir the vegetable mixture then place the sieve or steamer over the vegetables and cover the saucepan. Leave to cook gently for 30 minutes.

Stir the couscous to separate the grains, spoon on to four warm serving plates, spoon over the vegetable mixture and serve.

Tip:

Follow the packaging instructions carefully when preparing the couscous, the instructions can vary considerably. If desired increase the quantity of cumin and coriander by ½–1 teaspoon.

Spinach Pancakes

4 oz (120 g) plain flour
1 egg
½ pint (300 ml) skimmed milk
salt
2–3 oz (60–90 g) fresh young
spinach, washed, drained and
roughly chopped
3 tbs oil

SELECTIONS PER SERVING:

1 Bread
2 Fat
¼ Milk
¼ Vegetable
25 Optional Calories

CALORIES PER
SERVING: 250

SERVES 4

PREPARATION AND COOKING TIME: 25 MINUTES

Place the flour, egg and half the milk in a liquidiser and process until smooth. Add the remaining milk and a pinch of salt and process once again. Add the spinach, if necessary add a little at a time, and process until the spinach is very finely chopped.

Prove a small frying pan: generously sprinkle salt over the base of the pan, heat gently, tip out the salt then wipe thoroughly with a pad of kitchen paper. Heat a small amount of oil in the pan and then wipe round.

Heat about ¼ teaspoon oil in the pan. Stir the batter and tip a little batter into the pan whilst turning so it thinly coats the base. Cook over a moderate heat until the underside is golden to dark brown – cook the pancakes for a little longer than when using a conventional plain batter. Using a fish slice turn the pancake and cook the other side.

Transfer the pancake to a plate, cover and keep warm. Heat just under ¼ teaspoon oil in the pan, stir the batter and cook in the same way as described above. Continue until all the batter has been cooked. This quantity should be sufficient for 10 pancakes but as it takes practice to cook this batter aim for 8 or 9 for the first time.

Tip:

Serve these pancakes piping hot, sprinkled with 2 oz (60 g) crumbled feta or grated Parmesan cheese and folded into four. Alternatively roll round a filling of vegetables. Add ½ Protein to the Selections and increase Total Calories per serving to 285.

Left: Spinach Pancakes

6 oz (180 g) Brie cheese, rind
   removed and cubed
6 oz (180 g) Gruyère cheese,
   grated
2 tsps cornflour
1 clove garlic, halved
4 fl oz (120 ml) white wine
2 tbs dry sherry
4 fl oz (120 ml) skimmed milk
8 oz (240 g) French bread, cut
   into ½ inch (1.25 cm) cubes
pepper
freshly grated nutmeg

SELECTIONS PER SERVING:

2 Bread
3 Protein
50 Optional Calories

CALORIES PER
SERVING: 450

Cheese Fondue

SERVES 4
PREPARATION AND COOKING TIME: 25 MINUTES

Mix the cheeses together with the cornflour and set aside.

Rub the garlic round the inside of a fondue dish or a bowl resting on top of a saucepan of simmering water. Discard the garlic.

Pour the wine and sherry into a small saucepan and heat until steaming, pour into the fondue dish or bowl. Gradually add the cheese and cornflour, 3 tablespoons at a time. Cook over a very low heat until the cheese has melted then gradually stir in the milk. Continue stirring until the mixture is smooth.

While the Fondue is cooking toast the French bread under a moderate grill.

Season the Fondue with pepper and freshly grated nutmeg.

Serve in the fondue dish or pour into a warm serving bowl. Serve immediately with the French bread.

Tip:

Take care not to overheat the mixture or it will curdle or set in a hard lump!

Illustrated on page 166

2 tsps tomato ketchup
¼ tsp Worcestershire sauce
2 tbs mayonnaise
2 tbs low fat natural yogurt
1 tbs single cream
7 small sprigs of fresh basil
3 or 4 lettuce leaves, shredded
6 eggs, hard-boiled, shelled and
   halved

SELECTIONS PER SERVING:

1 Fat
1 Protein
¼ Vegetable
10 Optional Calories

Eggs in Tomato Mayonnaise

SERVES 6
PREPARATION AND COOKING TIME: 10 MINUTES PLUS COOLING

Blend together the tomato ketchup, Worcestershire sauce, mayonnaise, yogurt and cream. Finely chop one sprig of basil and stir into the mayonnaise mixture.

Arrange the lettuce on six small serving plates and place two egg halves on top of each. Spoon a little of the tomato mayonnaise over each half of egg, garnish with the sprigs of basil and serve.

CALORIES PER
SERVING: 115

Tip:

To hard-boil the eggs: place them in a saucepan, cover with cold water and bring to the boil. Boil for 10 minutes, drain, cool under running cold water and remove the shells. By following this method the eggs should not develop black rings round the yolks.

1 oz (30 g) margarine
1½ tbs flour
¼ pint (150 ml) skimmed milk
3 oz (90 g) well-flavoured
   cheese, e.g. mature Cheddar,
   Parmesan; finely grated
salt and pepper
freshly grated nutmeg
3 eggs, separated

SELECTIONS PER SERVING:

1½ Fat
1½ Protein
25 Optional Calories

CALORIES PER
SERVING: 230

Cheese Soufflé

SERVES 4

PREPARATION AND COOKING TIME: 50 MINUTES

Pre-heat the oven to 200°C, 400°F, Gas Mark 6.

Use a little margarine to grease a 7 inch (17.5 cm) soufflé dish.

Heat the remaining margarine in a saucepan, add the flour and remove from the heat. Gradually blend in the milk. Bring the sauce to the boil, stirring all the time, boil for 1–2 minutes. Stir in the cheese, season to taste with salt, pepper and freshly grated nutmeg. Mix in the egg yolks.

Place the egg whites in a bowl, add a pinch of salt and whisk until peaking. Using a metal spoon gently fold the egg whites into the cheese sauce then spoon into the soufflé dish.

Bake in the pre-heated oven for about 35 minutes until well-risen and golden brown. Serve immediately.

Variations:

Add an extra ½ tablespoon flour to the margarine when making the sauce and replace the 3 oz (90 g) cheese with 3 oz (90 g) finely chopped ham – the Selections will remain the same (Total Calories per serving 185).

or 1 oz (30 g) finely grated smoked cheese and 2 oz (60 g) finely chopped smoked ham – the Selections will remain the same (Total Calories per serving 200).

or 3 oz (90 g) very finely flaked cooked smoked haddock – the Selections would be 1½ Fat, 1 Protein, 30 Optional Calories. (Total Calories per serving 185.)

Illustrated on page 166

Left: Cheese Fondue (page 164)

Left: Cheese Soufflé (page 165)

Right: Pork and Vegetable Stew (page 168)

Pork and Vegetable Stew

14 oz (420 g) pork tenderloin
2 tsps oil
1 onion, finely chopped
1 clove garlic, finely chopped
1 large red pepper, deseeded
　　and cut into 1½ inch (4 cm)
　　lengths about ½ inch
　　(1.25 cm) wide
2 sticks celery, cut into 1½ inch
　　(4 cm) lengths about ½ inch
　　(1.25 cm) wide
1 tbs flour
8 oz (240 g) potatoes, cut into
　　1½ inch (4 cm) lengths about
　　½ inch (1.25 cm) wide
6 oz (180 g) mixture of carrots
　　and swede, cut into 1½ inch
　　(4 cm) lengths about ½ inch
　　(1.25 cm) wide
3 oz (90 g) drained canned
　　sweetcorn
4 oz (120 g) mixture of frozen
　　broad beans and peas
1 tbs vegetable or tomato purée
14 fl oz (420 ml) vegetable stock
salt and pepper

SELECTIONS PER SERVING:

1 Bread
½ Fat
3 Protein
1¾ Vegetable
10 Optional Calories

CALORIES PER
SERVING: 280

SERVES 4

PREPARATION AND COOKING TIME: 50 MINUTES

Place the pork tenderloin on the rack of a grill pan and cook under a moderate heat for about 7–8 minutes, turning once.

Heat the oil in a large saucepan, add the onion and garlic and stir-fry for 2–3 minutes. Add the red pepper and celery, stir round then cover the saucepan and leave over a low heat for 6–7 minutes.

Cut the pork in half along its length. Cut each half in thin slices.

Stir the flour into the onion mixture. Add all the vegetables and stir in the vegetable or tomato purée, stock and pork and bring to the boil. Stir the mixture well, season to taste with salt and pepper, cover the saucepan and leave to simmer gently for 30 minutes or until the pork and vegetables are cooked.

Tip:

If you wish use fresh broad beans or peas, allow 8–10 oz (240–300 g) unpodded weight.

Pork and Vegetable Stew *illustrated on previous page*

Vegetables with Polenta

1 pint (600 ml) water

4 oz (120 g) polenta

3 oz (90 g) well-flavoured hard
  cheese, e.g. 1 oz (30 g)
  Parmesan cheese and 2 oz
  (60 g) mature Cheddar
  cheese, grated

2 tsps oil

1 clove garlic, finely chopped

8 oz (240 g) leeks, thickly sliced

3 oz (90 g) fennel, thinly sliced

1 red pepper, deseeded and cut
  into ¾ inch (2 cm) squares

3 oz (90 g) okra, halved

4 oz (120 g) drained canned
  sweetcorn

9 oz (270 g) drained canned
  chick peas, plus 4 tbs liquid
  reserved from the can

1 tbs vegetable purée

15 oz (450 g) canned chopped
  tomatoes

¼ tsp dried mixed herbs

salt and pepper

SELECTIONS PER SERVING:

1 Bread
½ Fat
1½ Protein
3 Vegetable
25 Optional Calories

CALORIES PER
SERVING: 315

SERVES 4
PREPARATION AND COOKING TIME: 1 HOUR

Place the water in a 2 pint (1.2 litre), or larger, saucepan and bring to a rolling boil. Tip the polenta into the boiling water whilst stirring with a wooden spoon – if possible use a spoon with a fairly long handle as the polenta spits during cooking. Stir well and return to the boil. Cook over a gentle heat for 25–30 minutes until the mixture is extremely thick. Stir from time to time during the first 15 minutes then frequently during the last 10 minutes to prevent burning.

Dampen a chopping board with cold water. Remove the polenta from the heat and stir in about half the cheese. If you are using a mixture of Parmesan and Cheddar cheese add all the Parmesan and a little Cheddar. Tip the polenta out on to the board and spread until about ¾ inch (2 cm) thick. Level the surface with a damp knife. Leave until set, this will only take a few minutes.

Heat the oil in a saucepan, add the garlic and stir round then add the leeks, fennel, red pepper and okra. Cover the saucepan and leave over a low heat for 5–6 minutes.

Stir in all the remaining ingredients except the cheese. Season to taste. Stir well then cover the saucepan and leave over a low heat to simmer for 20–25 minutes.

Cut the polenta into eight triangles or using a fluted cutter cut into eight circles. If you choose to make round shapes cut seven circles then press the trimmings together and shape into the last round.

Spoon the hot vegetables into a flameproof dish, arrange the polenta shapes on top and sprinkle with the cheese. Cook under a hot grill until bubbling and beginning to brown.

Variation:

If you don't like polenta the vegetables taste delicious on their own. Serve them with 2 oz (60 g) fresh crusty bread or a 8 oz (240 g) baked jacket potato per serving. The Selections would be: 2 Bread, ½ Fat, 1½ Protein, 3 Vegetable, 25 Optional Calories (Total Calories per serving 355).

Cheese Salad with Creamy Dressing

1 oz (30 g) fromage frais
1 tsp skimmed milk
½ tsp Dijon mustard
1½ tbs mayonnaise
1 tbs thick single or double
   cream
6 oz (180 g) cheese, e.g. Edam,
   Double Gloucester, cut into
   ½ inch (1.25 cm) cubes
1 medium apple, roughly
   chopped
½ red pepper, deseeded and
   roughly chopped
½ yellow pepper, deseeded and
   roughly chopped
1 small courgette, roughly
   chopped
1 stick celery, sliced
4 or 5 spring onions, cut into
   ½–¾ inch (1.25–2 cm)
   diagonal slices

SELECTIONS PER SERVING:

1 Fat
1½ Protein
¾ Vegetable
35 Optional Calories

CALORIES PER
SERVING: 185

SERVES 4
PREPARATION: 10 MINUTES
NO COOKING REQUIRED

Stir the fromage frais together with the milk, mustard and mayonnaise. Blend in the cream.

Mix the cheese, apple and prepared vegetables together. Spoon the creamy dressing over the salad and stir to coat all the ingredients.

Tip:

Many supermarkets sell extra-thick single and double cream. Do not stir them more than necessary as the more they are stirred the thinner they become.

Potted Chicken

1 tbs margarine
1½ oz (45 g) onion, finely
   chopped
4 tsps flour
4 fl oz (120 ml) skimmed milk
½–¾ chicken stock cube
3 oz (90 g) cooked chicken,
   finely chopped
2 oz (60 g) curd cheese

SERVES 4
PREPARATION AND COOKING TIME: 30 MINUTES

Heat the margarine in a small saucepan, add the onion and stir over a moderate heat for 1 minute then reduce the heat and cook gently for about 10 minutes, stirring occasionally, until beginning to turn golden brown.

SELECTIONS PER SERVING:

½ Fat
1 Protein
30 Optional Calories

CALORIES PER
SERVING: 105

Do not allow to burn.

Add the flour to the saucepan and stir well then remove from the heat and gradually blend in the milk. Crumble half the stock cube into the milk, if the stock cube is not too salty add about three-quarters to the milk. Return to the heat and bring to the boil, stirring all the time. Boil for 3–4 minutes until very thick. Remove from the heat and allow to cool for 2–3 minutes.

Stir in the chicken and the curd cheese.

Spoon the chicken sauce into a small dish or ramekin and smooth over the top. Allow to cool then refrigerate until ready to serve.

Tip:

Serve as a sandwich spread or on toast with a mixed salad.

---

1 tbs margarine
1 onion, chopped
8 oz (240 g) celery, sliced
¼ tsp dried tarragon
6 fl oz (180 ml) chicken or vegetable stock
4 × 4 oz (120 g) skinned and boned chicken breasts

SELECTIONS PER SERVING:

½ Fat
3 Protein
1 Vegetable
10 Optional Calories

CALORIES PER
SERVING: 180

Chicken in Celery Sauce

SERVES 4
PREPARATION AND COOKING TIME: 55 MINUTES

Heat the margarine in a saucepan and stir-fry the onion for 2–3 minutes. Add the celery, stir round then mix in the tarragon and half the stock. Cover the saucepan and cook gently over a low heat for 15 minutes. Stir in the remaining stock, lay the chicken on top of the celery mixture, re-cover the saucepan and simmer gently for 25–30 minutes.

Remove the chicken from the saucepan and keep warm while completing the celery sauce.

Pour the celery mixture into a liquidiser and process to a purée. Return the purée to the saucepan and bring to the boil over a high heat, boil fiercely for 2–3 minutes until reduced to a thick consistency.

Leave the chicken in four pieces or cut into cubes then stir into the hot sauce and serve.

Tip:

Serve with a selection of brightly coloured vegetables such as carrots and broccoli. This recipe freezes well and can be reheated in the microwave oven. Freeze as a complete meal for four people or divide into individual portions.

3 lb (1.4 kg) spaghetti squash
**5 oz (150 g) well-flavoured hard
    cheese, e.g. mature Cheddar,
    grated**
**1 oz (30 g) Parmesan cheese,
    grated**
1 oz (30 g) fresh breadcrumbs

SELECTIONS PER SERVING:

1½ Protein
3 Vegetable
20 Optional Calories

CALORIES PER
SERVING: 215

'Spaghetti' Cheese Squash

SERVES 4
PREPARATION AND COOKING TIME: 50 MINUTES

Pre-heat the oven to 190°C, 375°F, Gas Mark 5.

Cut the squash in half along its length and scoop out the seeds. Place the halves in a large saucepan – it may be necessary to use two saucepans – cover with water and bring to the boil. Cook for 18–20 minutes until the flesh is tender. Drain the squash then run briefly under running cold water until cool enough to hold. Using a large spoon scrape the inside of the squash into a bowl – it will leave the skins in strands.

Stir both the cheeses into the bowl and mix well.

Spoon the 'Spaghetti' Cheese into an ovenproof dish, sprinkle over the breadcrumbs and bake in the pre-heated oven for 25 minutes until the crumbs are lightly golden.

Tip:

If you wish to make this recipe for two people it is worth remembering that many supermarkets will cut large squash in half if requested.

**1 lb 12 oz (840 g) butternut
    squash**
6 tbs low fat natural yogurt
salt and pepper

SELECTIONS PER SERVING:

1 Vegetable
10 Optional Calories

CALORIES PER
SERVING: 20

Butternut Squash Purée

SERVES 6
PREPARATION AND COOKING TIME: 20 MINUTES

Cut the squash in half and scoop out the seeds. Cut the skin off the squash then cut into 1½ inch (4 cm) cubes. Cook in boiling water for about 15 minutes until a knife will easily cut into the flesh.

Drain well and transfer to a liquidiser or food processor, add the yogurt and process to a purée. Season with salt and pepper to taste.

Variation:

Reduce the amount of yogurt to 2 tbs and mix in 4 oz (120 g) curd cheese. The Selections would be 1 Vegetable, 25 Optional Calories.

Parsnip and Apple Purée

1 lb (480 g) parsnips, sliced
1 medium cooking apple,
  peeled, cored and thickly
  sliced
2 tbs skimmed milk
salt and pepper
lemon juice

SELECTIONS PER SERVING:

½ Bread
25 Optional Calories

CALORIES PER
SERVING: 45

SERVES 6

PREPARATION AND COOKING TIME: 20 MINUTES

Place the parsnips in a saucepan and cover with boiling water, bring to the boil, cover the saucepan and cook for 8–9 minutes.

Place the apple in a steamer or metal sieve.

Set the steamer or sieve over the parsnips and cook for a further 4 minutes until the apple and parsnips are cooked – if necessary the apple can be removed and the parsnips cooked for a little longer.

Drain the parsnips and either place in a bowl and mash with the apple to form a purée or transfer the parsnips and apple to a liquidiser or food processor and process to a purée.

Add the skimmed milk and season well with salt, pepper and a little lemon juice, mix well and serve.

Tip:

This recipe freezes well. Put in a suitable container and store for up to 3 months.

Spinach and Potato Purée

1 lb 2 oz (540 g) potatoes, sliced
1 lb 2 oz (540 g) frozen chopped
  spinach
2 tbs single cream
salt and pepper
freshly grated nutmeg
1 tbs skimmed milk

SELECTIONS PER SERVING:

½ Bread
½ Vegetable
30 Optional Calories

CALORIES PER
SERVING: 105

SERVES 6

PREPARATION AND COOKING TIME: 20 MINUTES

Cook the potatoes in a saucepan of boiling water for about 15 minutes. Drain well.

Cook the spinach according to the packaging instructions, drain well by pressing it hard against the sides of a sieve – it should weigh about 9 oz (270 g) after sieving.

Either mash the potatoes in a bowl with the spinach then add the cream, salt and pepper and nutmeg to taste or put all the ingredients into a liquidiser or food processor and process to a purée. Add the skimmed milk to the purée and serve.

Tip:

For a dinner party make one third of each purée and serve in a tureen, garnished with fresh herbs.

Cheese and Potato Pie

2 lb (960 g) potatoes
salt
4 oz (120 g) curd cheese
3–4 tbs skimmed milk
½ oz (15 g) fresh chervil, finely
    chopped
½ oz (15 g) fresh chives, finely
    chopped
4 oz (120 g) hard cheese, e.g.
    Cheddar, Double Gloucester,
    grated
pepper
1 tomato, thinly sliced

SELECTIONS PER SERVING:

2 Bread
1½ Protein
5 Optional Calories

CALORIES PER
SERVING: 330

SERVES 4

PREPARATION AND COOKING TIME: 30 MINUTES

Cook the potatoes in boiling salted water, drain well. Mash them together with the curd cheese, milk and herbs. Reserve about ½ oz (15 g) of the hard cheese and mix the remainder into the mashed potatoes. Season with salt and pepper.

Spoon the potato mixture into a flameproof dish and roughen the surface with a fork. Arrange the tomato on top of the potato, sprinkle over the reserved cheese and cook under a hot grill until golden.

Variation:

Replace about one-third of the potatoes with the same weight of parsnips. The Bread Selection will remain the same.

Vegetable Frittata

1 tbs margarine
1 small onion, finely chopped
1 small red or green pepper, or a
    mixture, deseeded and cut
    into thin strips or half circles
1½ oz (45 g) broccoli florets,
    divided into very small florets
    and any stalks sliced
3 eggs
2 tbs skimmed milk
salt and pepper
2 button mushrooms, sliced or
    quartered
½ oz (15 g) cheese, grated

SELECTIONS PER SERVING:

1½ Fat
1½ Protein
1¼ Vegetable
20 Optional Calories

SERVES 2

PREPARATION AND COOKING TIME: 20 MINUTES

Heat the margarine in an 8 inch (20 cm) frying pan and stir-fry the onion and red or green pepper for about 4 minutes until softened.

Meanwhile blanch the broccoli in boiling water for 2½ minutes, drain well.

Beat the eggs together with the milk, season with salt and pepper.

Stir the well-drained broccoli and mushrooms into the frying pan, increase the heat and add the eggs. Using a fork draw the setting egg from the outside edge of the pan towards the centre for 1–2 minutes. Reduce the heat and leave to cook gently for about 10 minutes until the egg is almost set and you can see the underside is golden when the edge is slightly lifted.

Sprinkle the cheese over the Frittata and transfer to a very hot grill and cook for about 1 minute until the egg is completely set. Cut the Frittata in half and slide on to two warm serving plates.

CALORIES PER
SERVING: 240

Variation:

Serve the Frittata with 2 × 1½ oz (45 g) wedges of French bread each spread with 2 teaspoons of low fat spread. The Selections would be: 1½ Bread, 2 Fat, 1½ Protein, 1¼ Vegetable, 20 Optional Calories (Total Calories per serving 395).

---

3 oz (90 g) curd cheese
2 oz (60 g) smoked cod's roe
1 tsp skimmed milk
½ tsp horseradish sauce
½ oz (15 g) breadcrumbs, made from 2-day-old bread
lemon juice
18 small black olives
a few salad leaves, if possible a mixture of colours
1 tbs chopped fresh parsley to garnish

SELECTIONS PER SERVING:

45 Optional Calories

CALORIES PER
SERVING: 45

Curd Cheese and Olive Balls

SERVES 6
PREPARATION: 15 MINUTES
NO COOKING REQUIRED

Mash the curd cheese together with the cod's roe. Stir the milk and horseradish sauce together then mix into the curd cheese. Stir in the breadcrumbs to make a stiff, slightly sticky mixture. Add lemon juice to taste. If time allows refrigerate for 20–30 minutes, this will make the mixture a little firmer to handle.

Take a teaspoonful of the curd cheese mixture and press an olive into the centre. With your hands roll the curd cheese round the olive. Repeat with the remaining olives and curd cheese.

Arrange the salad leaves on each serving plate, lay the cheese balls on top and sprinkle with parsley.

Variation:

If preferred, small stuffed olives may be used in place of the black variety.

¾ oz (20 g) fresh yeast
approximately ¾ pint (450 ml)
    skimmed milk
1 lb 8 oz (720 g) strong
    wholemeal flour plus 1 tbs
1 tbs salt
1 oz (30 g) margarine
25 mg Vitamin C tablet
oil

SELECTIONS PER SERVING:

1 oz (30 g) slice = 1 Bread
80 Calories per slice

CALORIES PER LOAF
SERVING: 2560 per large loaf
          1280 per small loaf

'Short Time' Wholemeal Bread

1 LARGE OR 2 SMALL LOAVES
PREPARATION AND COOKING TIME: 1 HOUR PLUS RISING

Crumble the yeast into a jug. Heat the milk until hand hot then gradually blend it into the yeast.

Reserve 1 tablespoon flour, sieve the remainder together with the salt into a large mixing bowl; tip the bran remaining in the sieve into the bowl. Rub in the margarine.

Crush the Vitamin C tablet into the yeast mixture and stir well until it has dissolved. Make a well in the flour and pour the liquid into it. Mix together using a wooden spoon to form a soft dough, if necessary add a little more warm milk. Continue mixing with your hands until you have a dough that leaves the sides of the bowl clean and forms a ball.

Lightly flour a working surface with the 1 tablespoon flour and tip the dough on to it and knead well, draw about one-third of the dough up with your fingers and fold back on to the remaining two-thirds then press down firmly with the palm of your hand. Continue kneading in a rhythmic motion for about 10 minutes.

Grease one large or two small loaf tins with the oil and press the dough firmly into them. Cover dough with a lightly greased piece of polythene and leave in a warm place until doubled in size (about 30–40 minutes). Pre-heat the oven to 230°C, 450°F, Gas Mark 8. Remove polythene and bake in the pre-heated oven for 30–40 minutes.

Check the bread is cooked by turning upside down and tapping the base, it should sound hollow if cooked. Transfer to a wire rack and leave to cool.

Tip:

This method of breadmaking saves a great deal of time as it eliminates the second rising usually required. Bakers and some bakery departments in supermarkets sell fresh yeast but if you prefer, substitute ½ oz (15 g) dried and prepare it according to the packaging instructions.

Wholemeal Soda Bread

12 oz (360 g) plain wholemeal flour plus 1 tbs
½ tsp salt
1½ tsps bicarbonate of soda
9–10 fl oz (270–300 ml) buttermilk

SELECTIONS PER SERVING:

1 oz (30 g) slice = 1 Bread
80 Calories per slice

CALORIES PER LOAF
SERVING: 1185 per loaf

1 LOAF

PREPARATION AND COOKING TIME: 35 MINUTES

Pre-heat the oven to 220°C, 425°F, Gas Mark 7.

Lay a sheet of non-stick baking parchment on a baking sheet.

Reserve the 1 tablespoon flour, sieve the remainder with the salt and bicarbonate of soda into a large mixing bowl, tip the bran remaining in the sieve into the bowl. Add 9 fl oz (270 ml) buttermilk and mix with a fork. Add more buttermilk and mix until it forms a soft dough.

Sprinkle a working surface with 1–2 teaspoons flour and knead the dough lightly until smooth. Transfer to the baking sheet and using floured hands pat into a circle about 1–1½ inch (2.5–4 cm) thick. Cut a deep cross in the top.

Bake in the pre-heated oven for 20–25 minutes until cooked. Check the loaf is cooked by tapping the bottom, if it is cooked it should sound hollow. Transfer to a wire rack and leave until just warm. Serve whilst still warm.

Tip:

If you prefer a softer crust, wrap the loaf in a clean cloth and leave it to cool. This bread must be eaten while fresh, if it isn't all eaten the day it is made freeze it for the future.

Illustrated on page 179

Flapjacks

4 oz (120 g) margarine
4½ oz (135 g) soft brown sugar
1 tbs golden syrup
8 oz (240 g) rolled oats
½ tsp ground allspice

SELECTIONS PER SERVING:

½ Bread
1½ Fat
55 Optional Calories

CALORIES PER
SERVING: 165

MAKES 14

PREPARATION AND COOKING TIME: 30 MINUTES PLUS COOLING

Pre-heat the oven to 190°C, 375°F, Gas Mark 5.

Line a 7 × 11 inch (17.5 × 27.5 cm) Swiss-roll tin with non-stick baking parchment.

Gently heat the margarine, sugar and syrup in a saucepan. When the margarine has melted, stir in the oats and spice, mix well.

Transfer the mixture to the prepared tin and, using the back of a spoon, press down to level the surface.

Bake in the pre-heated oven for 20–25 minutes until golden brown. Set aside for about 5 minutes then mark into 14 fingers and leave in the tin until cold. When cold, cut completely through the Flapjack and remove from the tin.

Variation:

Add 2½ oz (75 g) raisins to the mixture before pressing into the tin, this will increase the Optional Calories to 70 per Flapjack (180 Calories per serving).

Shortbread Biscuits

2 oz (60 g) margarine
1 oz (30 g) caster sugar
few drops of vanilla essence
3 oz (90 g) plain flour plus 2 tsps

SELECTIONS PER SERVING:

1 Fat
45 Optional Calories

CALORIES PER
SERVING: 80

MAKES 10

PREPARATION AND COOKING TIME: 25 MINUTES

Pre-heat the oven to 160°C, 325°F, Gas Mark 3.

Line a baking sheet with non-stick baking parchment.

Cream the margarine and caster sugar together with the vanilla essence. Reserve 2 teaspoons flour, sieve the remainder into the creamed mixture and mix well to form a soft dough.

Sprinkle the reserved flour over the work surface and rolling pin. Roll the dough out until about ¼ inch (5 mm) thick. Cut into 10 biscuits using a 2½ inch (6.25 cm) round cutter. Re-roll the trimmings as necessary.

Place the biscuits on the prepared tin and prick with a fork. Bake in the pre-heated oven for about 15 minutes until lightly browned. Cool on a wire rack.

Wholemeal Soda Bread (page 177)

Gingernuts (page 177), Flapjacks and
Shortbread Biscuits

Gingernuts

4 oz (120 g) self-raising flour
2 tsps ground ginger
¼ tsp ground cinnamon
½ tsp bicarbonate of soda
2 oz (60 g) margarine
1 tbs clear honey
1 oz (30 g) soft brown sugar

SELECTIONS PER SERVING:

1 Fat
40 Optional Calories

CALORIES PER
SERVING: 80

MAKES 12
PREPARATION AND COOKING TIME: 25 MINUTES

Pre-heat the oven to 180°C, 350°F, Gas Mark 4.

Line a large baking sheet with non-stick baking parchment.

Sieve the flour, spices and bicarbonate of soda into a mixing bowl.

Gently heat the margarine, honey and sugar in a small saucepan until the margarine has melted and the sugar dissolved. Pour the melted margarine mixture into the flour and mix well.

Divide the mixture into twelve equal pieces and roll each piece into a small ball. Place them on the lined baking sheet and flatten slightly with the palm of your hand.

Bake in the pre-heated oven for about 15 minutes. Cool on a wire rack.

Tip:

To prevent the honey sticking to the measuring spoon rub a little oil all over the spoon then remove the honey from the pot and it will run cleanly into the saucepan.

Speedy Sandwich Cake

4 oz (120 g) margarine
4 oz (120 g) caster sugar
2 eggs
½ tsp grated lemon zest
4 oz (120 g) self-raising flour
1 tsp baking powder
3 tbs strawberry or raspberry
  jam
½ tsp icing sugar

SELECTIONS PER SERVING:

2 Fat
125 Optional Calories

CALORIES PER
SERVING: 200

SERVES 10
PREPARATION AND COOKING TIME: 45 MINUTES PLUS COOLING

Pre-heat the oven to 160–180°C, 325–350°F, Gas Mark 3–4.

Grease the sides of two 6½ inch (16.25 cm) sandwich tins with 1 teaspoon of the margarine, line the bases with non-stick baking parchment.

Place the remaining margarine, caster sugar, eggs and lemon zest into a large mixing bowl. Sieve the flour and baking powder and beat all the ingredients together using a wooden spoon for about 1½ minutes or use an electric hand-whisk and whisk for about 1 minute.

Divide the mixture evenly between the prepared tins, level the surfaces and bake in the pre-heated oven for 25–30 minutes. Allow to cool for 2–3 minutes then turn out on to a wire rack and leave until cold.

Sandwich the cakes together with the jam. Sieve the icing sugar over the cake.

Tip:

Cut the cake into ten slices and freeze for the future – this will avoid the temptation to eat several slices at one time!

Wholemeal Apricot Cake

4½ oz (135 g) margarine
3½ oz (105 g) caster sugar
2 eggs
6 oz (180 g) ready-to-eat dried
   apricots, chopped
1 oz (30 g) ground almonds
4 oz (120 g) self-raising
   wholemeal flour
2 oz (60 g) plain wholemeal
   flour
1½–2 tbs water

SELECTIONS PER SERVING:

½ Bread
2 Fat
½ Fruit
70 Optional Calories

CALORIES PER
SERVING: 210

SERVES 12

PREPARATION AND COOKING TIME: 1 HOUR 30 MINUTES PLUS COOLING

Pre-heat the oven to 160°C, 325°F, Gas Mark 3.

Line a 7 inch (17.5 cm) round cake tin with non-stick baking parchment.

Cream the margarine and sugar together in a mixing bowl until light in colour.

Lightly beat the eggs then add them to the creamed mixture a little at a time, beat well after each addition to prevent the mixture curdling. Stir in the apricots and the ground almonds.

Sieve the flours over the creamed mixture, tip the bran remaining in the sieve into the bowl. Gently fold the flour into the cake mixture and add sufficient water to give a consistency which drops easily from the spoon when lightly tapped on the side of the bowl.

Spoon the mixture into the prepared tin, level the surface and bake in the pre-heated oven for 1 hour 10 minutes or until the cake is golden brown and has shrunk a little from the side of the tin. Leave to cool in the tin for 15 minutes then turn out on to a wire rack and leave until cold.

Tip:

Wholemeal flour is sometimes called wholewheat. Don't confuse either of these with brown flour which contains far less of the wheat grain.

Simple Swiss Roll

2 eggs
3 oz (90 g) caster sugar
few drops of vanilla essence
2 oz (60 g) plain flour
1 tbs warm water
For the filling:
5 tbs jam

SELECTIONS PER SERVING:

115 Optional Calories

CALORIES PER
SERVING: 115

SERVES 8

PREPARATION AND COOKING TIME: 25 MINUTES

Pre-heat the oven to 220°C, 425°F, Gas Mark 7.

Line a 7½ inch × 11 inch (19 × 27.5 cm) shallow baking tray with non-stick baking parchment.

Break the eggs into a mixing bowl, reserve about ½ teaspoon caster sugar and add the remainder to the eggs. Add the vanilla essence and place the bowl over a saucepan of simmering water. Whisk the mixture until thick and creamy (about 10 minutes) – a trail should be left when the whisk is drawn over the surface. Remove the saucepan from the heat and continue whisking for 3–4 minutes.

Sieve the flour and, using a metal tablespoon, gently fold the flour and warm water into the mixture. Spoon the mixture evenly into the prepared tin, do not spread with a knife or the air will be knocked out of the mixture.

Bake in the pre-heated oven for 8–9 minutes or until golden brown and the cake springs back when gently pressed.

While the roll is cooking warm the jam and dip a cloth in cold water, wring out tightly.

Tip the cooked roll upside down on to the damp cloth. Peel off the baking parchment and trim a very thin piece off the long sides of the cake. Spread the sponge with the warm jam.

Mark about 1 inch (2.5 cm) along one of the short edges of the cake with a knife, do not cut completely through. Supporting the cake with the cloth, roll up as tightly as possible. Transfer to a wire rack to cool.

When cold transfer the roll to a serving plate and sprinkle over the reserved sugar.

Tip:

To help prevent the bowl slipping while whisking, lay a cloth over the pan of simmering water then rest the bowl on the cloth.

Sticky Cinnamon Buns

4 oz (120 g) self-raising flour
   plus ½ tbs
½ tsp baking powder
1½ tbs margarine
finely grated zest of ½ a lemon
approximately 4 tbs skimmed
   milk
½ oz (15 g) soft brown sugar
¾ tsp ground cinnamon
1 tbs golden syrup

SELECTIONS PER SERVING:

½ Bread
½ Fat
20 Optional Calories

CALORIES PER
SERVING: 90

MAKES 8

PREPARATION AND COOKING TIME: 35 MINUTES

Pre-heat the oven to 220°C, 425°F, Gas Mark 7.

Sieve 4 oz (120 g) of the flour and the baking powder into a large mixing bowl, add 1 tablespoon margarine (if possible margarine which has been stored in the freezer) and rub into the flour using your fingertips. Stir in the lemon zest and gradually mix in the milk to form a soft dough.

Sprinkle half the remaining flour on a sheet of non-stick baking parchment, sprinkle the remainder over a rolling pin. Lightly knead the dough, just enough to make it smooth, then roll out to a rectangle 7 × 5½ inch (17.5 × 14 cm).

Spread the remaining margarine over the dough, leaving about ½ inch (1.25 cm) clear along one of the longer sides. Mix the brown sugar and cinnamon together then sprinkle over the margarine. Brush the clear margin of dough with a little water. Using the paper as support, roll up the dough from one of its longer sides towards the side with the margin of clear dough. Using a very sharp knife cut the dough into eight slices.

Lay a piece of non-stick baking parchment on a baking sheet and arrange the circles, cut-side uppermost on the paper. Leave a space at least ¾ inch (2 cm) between each bun. Bake in the pre-heated oven for 12 minutes until light golden brown.

While the buns are cooking spoon the syrup into a small bowl and stand it in a saucepan of simmering water. Remove the buns from the oven and leave for 2–3 minutes until cool enough to handle. Brush some of the warm syrup over the sides of the buns then place them on a serving plate and brush the tops with the remaining syrup. Serve warm.

Tip:

If your knife sticks to the dough while cutting, sprinkle the blade with a little flour.

Banana Nut Bars

2 oz (60 g) margarine
3 oz (90 g) caster or soft brown
   sugar
2 medium bananas, chopped
6 oz (180 g) plain flour
1½ tsps baking powder
2 eggs, lightly beaten
1½ oz (45 g) walnuts, roughly
   chopped

SELECTIONS PER SERVING:

½ Fat
100 Optional Calories

CALORIES PER
SERVING: 120

MAKES 16
PREPARATION AND COOKING TIME: 45 MINUTES

Pre-heat the oven to 160°C, 325°F, Gas Mark 3.

Line a shallow tin, about 7 × 11 inch (17.5 × 27.5 cm) with non-stick baking parchment.

Cream the margarine together with the sugar. Mash the banana and stir into the creamed mixture.

Sieve the flour together with the baking powder. Add the eggs, nuts and flour to the banana mixture and beat all the ingredients together.

Spoon the cake mixture into the prepared tin, level the surface and bake in the pre-heated oven for 30–35 minutes or until firm to touch and beginning to shrink from the sides of the tin. Allow to cool for 3–4 minutes then turn out of the tin and carefully peel off the paper.

Leave to cool on a wire rack. When cold cut into sixteen pieces.

Tip:

If desired use wholemeal flour in place of white and add a good pinch of cinnamon.

Chocolate Nutties

3 oz (90 g) self-raising flour
1 oz (30 g) cocoa
¾ tsp baking powder
2½ oz (75 g) Demerara sugar
1 egg
few drops of vanilla essence
3 tbs skimmed milk
1 tbs margarine
3 tbs smooth peanut butter

SELECTIONS PER SERVING:

65 Optional Calories

CALORIES PER
SERVING: 65

MAKES 18
PREPARATION AND COOKING TIME: 30 MINUTES

Pre-heat the oven to 180°C, 350°F, Gas Mark 4.

Line two baking sheets with non-stick baking parchment.

Sieve the flour, cocoa and baking powder into a large mixing bowl. Make a well in the flour and add all the remaining ingredients. Beat the mixture with a wooden spoon until evenly mixed and a stiff but sticky consistency – like a very stiff cake mixture.

Leave the mixture for 1 minute, it will become slightly stiffer, then take teaspoons full of the mixture and very lightly roll between the palms of your hands. Place the balls on the lined baking sheets and press lightly with the prongs of a fork to flatten.

Bake in the pre-heated oven for 18–20 minutes until firm to touch. Transfer to a wire rack and leave until cold.

Tip:

Dip the prongs of the fork in cold water after flattening three or four Nutties, this will help prevent the prongs sticking.

Sultana Scones

MAKES 8

PREPARATION AND COOKING TIME: 40 MINUTES

8 oz (240 g) plain flour plus 1 tbs
pinch of salt
4 tsps baking powder
2 oz (60 g) margarine
4 oz (120 g) sultanas
grated zest of ½ an orange
2 eggs
3 tbs skimmed milk

SELECTIONS PER SERVING:

1 Bread
1½ Fat
½ Fruit
20 Optional Calories

CALORIES PER
SERVING: 210

Reserve 1 tablespoon flour, sieve the remainder with the salt and baking powder into a large mixing bowl. Rub in the margarine (if possible margarine which has been stored in the freezer) with your fingertips until the mixture resembles fresh breadcrumbs. Stir in the sultanas and orange zest then make a well in the centre.

Lightly beat the eggs and 2 tablespoons milk, reserve 2 teaspoons of the mixture and pour the remainder into the well. Mix with a round-bladed knife to form a soft, but not sticky, dough, adding more milk as necessary.

Dust the working surface and a rolling pin with the reserved flour. Knead the dough lightly until smooth then roll out into a circle about 8 inch (20 cm) diameter.

Transfer the dough circle to a piece of non-stick baking parchment resting on a baking sheet and leave to stand for 10–15 minutes. Pre-heat the oven to 220°C, 425°F, Gas Mark 7. Brush the circle with the reserved egg and mark into eight wedges. Bake in the pre-heated oven for 15–20 minutes until golden. Leave to cool on a wire rack.

Tip:

Serve the scones warm or on the same day as baking. If desired leave until cold and cut into single wedges and freeze.

GUESTS ARE COMING

There is nothing nicer than celebrating a special occasion with a lovely meal. Whether you are inviting one or two guests for dinner or arranging a buffet party for several people, the key to success is careful planning. Decide how many guests you will invite and what type of dinner party or meal you wish to have. It is very easy to fall into the trap of making elaborately rich dishes with lashings of cream which leave your guests feeling over full and uncomfortable, let alone worried about their waistlines. If children are going to be at the meal make sure there is something they will like to eat. Remember, don't be over ambitious. If you aren't used to entertaining begin by inviting just a few people and choose a menu you know you can prepare easily. As you gain confidence you can increase the number of guests and become a little more adventurous with the choice of recipes.

Once you have invited your guests (and always ask them if they have any allergies or particular likes or dislikes to any foods) plan the whole meal including where you will shop for the ingredients, how you will decorate the table and what drinks you will serve. Always try to choose dishes which complement each other. At an elaborate dinner party, for instance, you could offer Duo of Carrot and Watercress Soup (page 190) followed by Sole Fillets with Prawns and Asparagus (page 205) accompanied by boiled new potatoes, broccoli, celery and carrots, and Chilled Lemon Soufflé (page 221). And after you have planned everything and prepared the recipes as well as the house, you will be able to relax and enjoy the occasion as much as everyone else.

Canapé Platter

SERVES 6

PREPARATION AND COOKING TIME: 30 MINUTES PLUS CHILLING

Anchovy Toasties

3 thin slices white bread, toasted
3 anchovy fillets
1 oz (30 g) curd cheese
1 drained canned pimento, cut into small strips

Cut the toast into different shapes with pastry cutters. (The total weight of six shapes should be 1½ oz (45 g).)

Pound the anchovy fillets to a paste with the rounded end of a rolling pin in a small bowl.

A short while before serving mix the anchovy paste with the curd cheese. Spread the mixture over the toast and garnish with the pimento strips.

Turkey and Asparagus Mini Roulades

4 tsps low fat spread
4 tsps mayonnaise
2 × 1 oz (30 g) slices of bread, trimmed of crusts
2 × ¼ oz (7 g) wafer-thin slices smoked turkey (American-style)
2 asparagus spears

Mash the low fat spread together with the mayonnaise, spread each slice of bread with the mixture and top with a turkey slice.

Place an asparagus spear along one side of the bread then roll up tightly, Swiss-roll style. Wrap tightly in clingfilm and leave for 3 hours or more.

A short while before serving cut each roll into six thin slices.

Tip:

This recipe works well with cooked, fresh, canned or frozen asparagus.

Illustrations on previous page: Asparagus Mousse (page 192), Beef in Wine and Juniper Sauce (page 200) and Black Forest Roll (page 213)

Tomato Cups

3 anchovy fillets
6 cherry tomatoes, halved
6 large black olives, halved

Cut each anchovy fillet into six and put a piece on each tomato half then lay half an olive on top.

Quail's Eggs with Celery Salt

6 quail's eggs
celery salt

Put the eggs in a saucepan of boiling water, boil for 4 minutes then cool under running cold water.

Leave the eggs whole or remove the shells, cut in half and sprinkle with a little celery salt.

Pumpernickel and Hummus

3 oz (90 g) drained canned chick
  peas, 1–2 tbs liquid reserved
1 tsp tahini
1 tsp olive oil
garlic purée
lemon juice
3 × ½ oz (15 g) slices of
  pumpernickel
paprika
To serve:
12 large stuffed or black olives
fresh herbs
a few gherkins

Put the chick peas into a liquidiser or food processor together with the reserved liquid, tahini, olive oil and garlic purée (enough to cover the tip of a knife). Blend to the consistency of mayonnaise. Taste and add lemon juice.

Spread the hummus on the pumpernickel slices, sprinkle with a little paprika then cut the slices in half.

Arrange the prepared canapés on a platter. Garnish with the olives, sprigs of herbs and gherkins.

SELECTIONS PER SERVING:

1 Bread
1 ½ Fat
½ Protein
½ Vegetable
35 Optional Calories

CALORIES PER
SERVING: 165

Tip:

The Total Selections given here are based on one sixth of each recipe per person.

If you prefer, just one of the canapé recipes may be served, but remember to calculate the Selections carefully.

Duo of Carrot and Watercress Soup

For the Carrot Soup:
½ tbs oil
1 onion, chopped
1 lb (480 g) carrots, sliced
2 inch (5 cm) strip of lemon zest
16 fl oz (480 ml) vegetable stock
lemon juice
salt and pepper

For the Watercress Soup:
½ tbs oil
4 oz (120 g) leeks, chopped
8 oz (240 g) watercress, roughly
    chopped
¾ pint (450 ml) vegetable stock
2 tbs cornflour
¼ pint (150 ml) skimmed milk
salt and pepper

SELECTIONS PER SERVING:

½ Fat
1¾ Vegetable
20 Optional Calories

CALORIES PER
SERVING: 75

SERVES 6

PREPARATION AND COOKING TIME: 50 MINUTES

First prepare the Carrot Soup and while that is cooking prepare and cook the Watercress Soup.

Heat the oil in a saucepan, add the onion and stir round then cover the saucepan and cook over a low heat for 4 minutes. Add the carrots, lemon zest and vegetable stock to the saucepan, bring to the boil, reduce the heat, cover and leave to simmer for 30 minutes.

Prepare the Watercress Soup. Heat the oil in a saucepan, add the leeks and stir over a low heat for 2 minutes. Add 2–3 oz (60–90 g) watercress, stir round, cover the saucepan and leave the cress to soften then add the remainder. Pour in the stock and bring to the boil, cover the saucepan and leave to simmer for 25 minutes.

Allow the Carrot Soup to cool for a few minutes, pour into a liquidiser or food processor (leave the lemon zest in the soup) and process to a purée. Pour the soup back into the saucepan.

Process the Watercress Soup in a liquidiser or food processor to a purée then pour back into the saucepan. Blend the cornflour together with the milk and stir into the soup. Bring to the boil stirring all the time, boil for 1–2 minutes.

Reheat the Carrot Soup. Adjust the seasonings of both soups adding lemon juice and salt and pepper to the carrot and a little salt and pepper to the watercress.

Put the soups into separate jugs then pour into each serving bowl from opposite sides of the bowl.

Tip:

Each individual soup makes approximately 1½ pints (900 ml) which is sufficient for three or four servings but remember to adjust the Selections as necessary.

Right: Duo of Carrot and Watercress Soup

Asparagus Mousse

14 oz (420 g) asparagus, stalks
    trimmed and scales removed
1 tbs margarine
1 tsp chopped onion
1 tbs flour
¼ pint (150 ml) whole milk
1½ tsps finely chopped fresh dill
2 tbs double cream
salt and pepper
lemon juice
2 tbs hot weak stock
1 tbs gelatine
1 egg white

SELECTIONS PER SERVING:

½ Fat
1¼ Vegetable
60 Optional Calories

CALORIES PER
SERVING: 115

*Illustrated on
pages 186/187*

SERVES 4

PREPARATION AND COOKING TIME: 20 MINUTES PLUS SETTING

Place the asparagus in a steamer and cook for 8–10 minutes or until tender.

Melt the margarine in a small saucepan, add the onion and stir-fry for 1–2 minutes. Stir in the flour then remove from the heat and gradually blend in the milk. Add the dill then bring to the boil, stirring all the time, boil for 1–2 minutes.

Transfer the asparagus to a liquidiser, add the sauce and cream and process to a purée. Pour into a bowl and season to taste with salt and pepper and lemon juice.

Spoon the stock into a cup, sprinkle in the gelatine and stir until dissolved – if necessary stand the cup in a saucepan of simmering water. Stir the dissolved gelatine into the purée and leave until beginning to set.

Whisk the egg white with a pinch of salt until peaking, then carefully fold into the purée. Spoon the mixture into four ramekins and chill until set.

Tip:

To freeze: place the ramekins, uncovered, in the freezer. When frozen wrap in a double layer of foil or transfer to a suitable airtight container.

Mushrooms Marinated in Wine and Garlic

1 tbs olive oil
2 cloves garlic, finely chopped
8 spring onions, thinly sliced
14 oz (420 g) very tiny button
    mushrooms (about 100)
4 fl oz (120 ml) dry white wine
2–3 inch (5–7.5 cm) strip of
    lemon zest
1 tsp lemon juice
pinch cayenne pepper
4 tbs chopped fresh coriander
salt
coriander leaves to garnish

SERVES 6

PREPARATION AND COOKING TIME: 15 MINUTES
PLUS MARINATING

Heat the oil in a saucepan, add the garlic and stir-fry over a gentle heat for 2 minutes, do not allow to brown. Add the spring onions and stir-fry for 1 minute. Add the mushrooms and stir round for 1–2 minutes then mix in the wine, the lemon zest, lemon juice, cayenne and chopped coriander.

To serve:

6 × 1 oz (30 g) pieces of wholemeal French bread

SELECTIONS PER SERVING:

1 Bread
½ Fat
1 Vegetable
15 Optional Calories

CALORIES PER
SERVING: 105

Cover the saucepan and cook gently over a low heat for 2–3 minutes.

Remove the lid from the saucepan and boil for 4–5 minutes. Transfer to a non-metallic bowl and leave until cool. Cover and chill for several hours or overnight, stirring occasionally.

Remove the lemon zest, season with salt and spoon into six ramekins. Garnish with a few whole coriander leaves and serve with the French bread to mop up all the juices.

Tip:

Do not try to peel the skins from the mushrooms, simply wash them well then wipe with a cloth.

---

4 oz (120 g) very thin green beans, topped, tailed and halved
1 large tomato, skinned, deseeded and chopped
2 oz (60 g) beansprouts
½ red pepper, deseeded and cut into thin strips
½ yellow pepper, deseeded and cut into thin strips
10 small black olives, stoned and chopped
6 anchovy fillets
6 tbs low fat natural yogurt
lemon juice
a few lettuce leaves, finely shredded
1 egg, hard-boiled and finely chopped

SELECTIONS PER SERVING:

1 Vegetable
30 Optional Calories

CALORIES PER
SERVING: 40

Green Bean and Anchovy Salad

SERVES 6

PREPARATION AND COOKING TIME: 20 MINUTES

Cook the beans for 3 minutes, drain. Mix the beans, tomato, bean sprouts, peppers and olives together in a bowl.

Rinse the anchovy fillets under running cold water. Using a pestle and mortar pound the anchovy fillets to a paste with 1–2 teaspoons yogurt. Alternatively place them in a small bowl and pound with the rounded end of a rolling pin. Stir the remaining yogurt into the anchovy paste and season with a little lemon juice, stir into the salad and toss well.

Arrange the lettuce leaves in serving glasses or on small serving plates, spoon the bean salad in the centre. Garnish with the chopped egg.

Tip One:

To skin tomatoes cover with boiling water for 30–40 seconds, drain then slip off the skins.

Tip Two:

Do not add salt when cooking the beans or mashing the anchovy dressing, the anchovies are very salty.

1 lb 8 oz (720 g) calabrese
  broccoli, stalks chopped and
  divided into florets
½ pint (300 ml) whole milk
2 tbs weak vegetable stock
5 tsps gelatine
4 oz (120 g) smoked salmon,
  chopped
4 tbs low fat natural yogurt
4 tbs soured cream
1 tbs finely chopped fresh chives
3–4 tsps lemon juice
salt and pepper

SELECTIONS PER SERVING:

½ Protein
1 Vegetable
45 Optional Calories

CALORIES PER
SERVING: 80

Broccoli and Smoked Salmon Mousse

SERVES 8

PREPARATION AND COOKING TIME: 25 MINUTES

PLUS SETTING AND CHILLING

Boil or steam the broccoli until cooked, drain well. Transfer to a liquidiser or food processor, add the milk and process to a purée. Pour into a bowl.

Spoon the stock into a cup, sprinkle in the gelatine then stand the cup in a saucepan of simmering water until the gelatine has dissolved.

Mix the salmon with the yogurt, cream and chives.

Stir the dissolved gelatine into the broccoli purée, add the yogurt mixture and season to taste with lemon juice, salt and pepper.

Spoon the mixture into eight ramekins and chill until set.

Tip:

Freezing is not recommended. It causes the top of the mousse to darken.

---

1 medium papaya, deseeded
½ medium Ogen melon,
  deseeded
½ medium Cantaloupe melon,
  deseeded
½ medium Galia melon,
  deseeded
2 tbs frozen concentrated
  orange juice, thawed
4 tbs port wine

SELECTIONS PER SERVING:

1 Fruit
10 Optional Calories

CALORIES PER
SERVING: 60

Mixed Melon and Papaya in Port and Orange

SERVES 6

PREPARATION AND COOKING TIME: 10 MINUTES

PLUS 2 HOURS MARINATING

Scoop out the flesh from the papaya and melons with a baller or teaspoon.

Place the papaya and melon balls in a bowl. Stir the orange juice and port wine together, spoon over the fruit and leave to marinate for 2 hours, or longer. Arrange in glass serving dishes and serve.

Tip:

Choose melons with a variety of different coloured flesh, for example, Cantaloupe (green), Charentais (golden yellow), to make an attractive appetizer, the total weight of the prepared melon should be 15 oz (450 g).

Prawn and Chicken Cups with Chives

SERVES 6

PREPARATION AND COOKING TIME: 35 MINUTES PLUS COOLING

3½ oz (105 g) plain flour plus ½ tbs
pinch of salt
3½ tbs margarine
1 oz (30 g) red pepper, deseeded and cut into fine strips ¾ inch (2 cm) long
1 oz (30 g) courgette, cut into fine strips ¾ inch (2 cm) long
2 oz (60 g) peeled prawns, roughly chopped
1 oz (30 g) cooked chicken, chopped
1 oz (30 g) fromage frais
1 tsp tomato ketchup
lemon juice
salt and pepper
1 large crisp lettuce leaf, shredded
1 tsp chopped fresh chives
selection of salad leaves

SELECTIONS PER SERVING:

½ Bread
1½ Fat
¼ Vegetable
45 Optional Calories

CALORIES PER SERVING: 150

Pre-heat the oven to 200°C, 400°F, Gas Mark 6.

Sieve the 3½ oz (105 g) flour with the salt into a bowl. Rub in the margarine (if possible margarine that has been stored in the freezer) until the mixture resembles fresh breadcrumbs. Add 3½ teaspoons ice-cold water and use a round-bladed knife to form a dough. Add a little more water if necessary.

Dust the rolling pin and working surface with the remaining flour. Roll out the pastry to form a rectangle about 5 × 7½ inch (12.5 × 19 cm). Cut the rectangle into six squares then press the squares lightly into six small pattie tins – leave the corners pointing above the edge of the tins. Prick the base of the squares once or twice with the prongs of a fork then cook in the pre-heated oven for about 15 minutes or until light brown. Remove from the oven, transfer to a wire rack and leave until cold.

Mix together the red pepper, courgette, prawns and chicken. Stir in the fromage frais and tomato ketchup. Season to taste with a little lemon juice, salt and pepper.

Fill the pastry cases a short while before serving. Place a little lettuce in each case, spoon the prawn and chicken mixture on top and sprinkle with the chives. Arrange the salad leaves on a serving plate and sit the Prawn and Chicken Cups on top.

Tip:

Spoon a little margarine into an ice-cube tray and freeze; it is much easier to rub in soft margarine which has been frozen.

2½ lb (1.2 kg) boned rolled leg
   of lamb
5 large cloves garlic, cut in half
   lengthways
few sprigs of rosemary, cut into
   10 × 1 inch (2.5 cm) pieces
2 medium cooking apples,
   peeled, cored and roughly
   chopped
5 oz (150 g) redcurrants
2 tbs water
½ tbs cornflour
2½ tbs sugar

SELECTIONS PER SERVING:

3 Protein
45 Optional Calories

CALORIES PER
SERVING: 200

Lamb with Apple and Redcurrant Sauce

SERVES 8

PREPARATION AND COOKING TIME: 3 HOURS

Pre-heat the oven to 180°C, 350°F, Gas Mark 4.

With the point of a sharp knife, make ten slits through the skin of the lamb, about ¾ inch (2 cm) long and put slivers of garlic and sprigs of rosemary in these cuts.

Lay a large piece of foil across a baking sheet, place a rack on top and rest the joint on the rack. Draw the foil up to cover the lamb and place in the pre-heated oven for 1 hour. Open the foil and continue cooking at 220°C, 425°F, Gas Mark 7 for 1 hour 30 minutes–1 hour 40 minutes until the lamb is a little pink in the centre. Leave to rest for 10 minutes then carve into thin slices, allowing 3 oz (90 g) meat per person, and arrange the slices on a warmed serving dish.

While the meat is cooking make the sauce. Place the apples and redcurrants in a saucepan with 1½ tablespoons of water, cover and cook over a low heat for 10–12 minutes. Blend the cornflour to a smooth paste with about ½ tablespoon water, stir into the fruit, add the sugar and bring to the boil, stirring all the time. Boil for 1–2 minutes. Reheat the sauce just before serving, pour into a bowl and serve with a spoon or ladle.

Tip:

If you prefer, the joint may be cooked on the bone. Use a meat thermometer for cooking accuracy.

Mixed Nut and Chick Pea Cutlets

3 oz (90 g) mixture of nut
    kernels, e.g. almonds,
    walnuts, peanuts; chopped
1 tbs sunflower seeds
1 tbs sesame seeds
1 lb 2 oz (540 g) well-drained
    canned chick peas
2 eggs
2 tbs peanut butter, smooth or
    crunchy
3 tbs oil
1 clove garlic, finely chopped
1 large onion, finely chopped
1½ oz (45 g) flour
1 tbs skimmed milk
2½ oz (75 g) dried breadcrumbs

SELECTIONS PER SERVING:

½ Bread
1½ Fat
2 Protein
¼ Vegetable
35 Optional Calories

CALORIES PER
SERVING: 270

SERVES 8
PREPARATION AND COOKING TIME: 45 MINUTES

Pre-heat the oven to 200°C, 400°F, Gas Mark 6.

Spread the nuts and seeds evenly over a baking sheet, then cook in the pre-heated oven for 8–10 minutes or until light golden brown.

While the nuts and seeds are cooking place the chick peas and one egg in a liquidiser or food processor and process to a thick purée. Transfer the purée to a bowl and mix in the peanut butter.

Heat ½ tablespoon oil in a saucepan, add the garlic and onion, stir round then cover and cook over a low heat for 5–6 minutes, stirring occasionally until soft. Stir the onion and garlic, nuts and seeds into the chick pea mixture. Divide the mixture into eight.

Spoon the flour on to one plate. Lightly beat the remaining egg with the milk and pour on to a second plate. Sprinkle half the breadcrumbs on to a sheet of greaseproof paper or non-stick baking parchment.

Dip one-eighth of the chick pea mixture into the flour and using your hands and a palette knife, form it into a cutlet. Coat with the egg and milk and then the breadcrumbs. This is made easier if you use the paper to lift the crumbs up to coat the sides of the cutlet then turn it over and coat the other side. Continue to make eight cutlets, topping up the breadcrumbs when necessary.

Heat half the remaining oil in a large frying pan and cook half the cutlets for 4–5 minutes on each side or until crisp and brown. Transfer to a plate and keep warm while cooking the other four cutlets in the remaining oil.

Tip:

If time allows place the chick pea and nut mixture in the freezer for 25–30 minutes so it is firmer and easier to handle.

Chicken Roulades with Spinach and Anchovies

6 × 3½ oz (105 g) boned and
skinned chicken breasts
14 oz (420 g) frozen leaf
spinach
1 × 1¾ oz (50 g) can anchovies
½ tsp garlic purée
4 tbs vermouth

SELECTIONS PER SERVING:

½ Fat
2½ Protein
¾ Vegetable
30 Optional Calories

CALORIES PER
SERVING: 140

SERVES 6

PREPARATION AND COOKING TIME: 1 HOUR 20 MINUTES

Pre-heat the oven to 180°C, 350°F, Gas Mark 4.

Cut horizontally through each chicken breast without cutting it completely in half. Lay the breast between two pieces of clingfilm and, using a rolling pin or steak hammer, beat until ⅛–¼ inch (2.5–5 mm) thick. Repeat with the other chicken breasts.

Cook the spinach according to the packaging instructions. Using a slotted spoon transfer the cooked spinach to a plate. Cover with a second plate and press hard to remove excess water.

Drain the anchovies, reserve the oil. Pound the anchovy fillets with a pestle and mortar or with a rolling pin, add 1 tablespoon of the reserved anchovy oil and the garlic purée and pound again.

Chop the well-drained spinach and mix together with the anchovy mixture.

Spread the anchovy mixture over each of the chicken breasts then roll them up and secure with cocktail sticks. Transfer the chicken rolls to an ovenproof dish, pour over the vermouth and cover with a piece of foil. Cook in the pre-heated oven for 1 hour. Remove the cocktail sticks and slice the chicken with a very sharp knife, arrange on a warm plate and serve.

Tip:

Do not substitute frozen *chopped* spinach, it does not have the texture required for this recipe.

Right: Chicken Roulades with Spinach and Anchovies

1 lb 5 oz (630 g) braising steak, cubed
6 fl oz (180 ml) Burgundy or dry red wine
8 fl oz (240 ml) water or stock
1 tbs oil
24 shallots, peeled
1½ tbs flour
9 oz (270 g) baby corn on the cob
4 anchovy fillets, chopped
6 juniper berries, crushed
1 clove garlic, crushed
bay leaf
salt and pepper

SELECTIONS PER SERVING:

½ Bread
½ Fat
3 Protein
½ Vegetable
35 Optional Calories

CALORIES PER SERVING: 230

Beef in Wine and Juniper Sauce

SERVES 6
PREPARATION AND COOKING TIME: 2 HOURS 15 MINUTES
PLUS COOLING TIME

Pre-heat the oven to 160°C, 325°F, Gas Mark 3.

Put the braising steak in a saucepan, add the wine and water or stock and bring to the boil over a low heat. Simmer for 2–3 minutes then leave to cool and skim off the fat which rises to the surface.

Heat the oil in a flameproof casserole, add the shallots and brown all over, stirring all the time. Sprinkle in the flour and stir well then add all the remaining ingredients.

Bring to the boil over a low heat, stir then cover the casserole and cook in the pre-heated oven for 2 hours.

Tip:

This recipe can be made ahead of time and stored overnight in the refrigerator or frozen for the future. If you choose to freeze, add 3–4 tablespoons stock when reheating. The meat becomes more tender if marinated in the wine for several hours.

Illustrated on pages 186/187

4 × 4½ oz (135 g) trout fillets
For the stuffing:
4 tsps margarine
6 tbs chopped spring onions
3 oz (90 g) watercress, finely chopped
3 oz (90 g) mushrooms, finely chopped
3 oz (90 g) fresh breadcrumbs
salt and pepper
1 tsp lemon juice
lemon wedges and sprigs of watercress to garnish

Roulade of Trout with Mushrooms and Watercress

SERVES 4
PREPARATION AND COOKING TIME: 40 MINUTES

Pre-heat the oven to 190°C, 375°F, Gas Mark 5.

To skin the trout fillets: place the fish skin-side down, and hold the tail, cut under the flesh at the tail-end and, using a sawing motion, gradually work up the fish to remove the skin. Repeat with each fillet.

Heat 3 teaspoons of the margarine in a saucepan and stir-fry the spring onions for 2 minutes. Add the watercress and mushrooms and stir-fry for another 3 minutes. Remove from the heat, mix in the breadcrumbs and season to taste with salt and pepper.

½ Bread
1 Fat
3½ Protein
¾ Vegetable
20 Optional Calories

CALORIES PER
SERVING: 265

Lay the fillets flat, skinned side up, and sprinkle with the lemon juice. Spread an equal quantity of stuffing on each fillet and roll up the fish from the head to the tail end and secure with cocktail sticks.

Place the rolled trout fillets on a large piece of foil greased with the remaining margarine, fold over the foil to seal. Bake in the pre-heated oven for 20 minutes.

To serve, remove the cocktail sticks and garnish the fillets with lemon wedges and sprigs of watercress.

Tip:

Serve the trout with 4 oz (120 g) baby new potatoes and 3 oz (90 g) crisp broccoli florets per serving but remember to add 1 Bread and 1 Vegetable Selection, and increase Total Calories per serving to 355.

---

15 oz (450 g) canned chopped
    tomatoes
½ tsp garlic purée
2 oz (60 g) spring onions, sliced
2 oz (60 g) cashew kernels
2 oz (60 g) bread
2 oz (60 g) sage Derby cheese,
    finely grated
2 tbs white wine
6 oz (180 g) drained canned
    flageolet beans
13¾ oz (410 g) drained can
    artichoke bottoms, rinsed and
    roughly chopped
4 oz (120 g) wafer-thin sliced
    smoked ham (American-
    style), chopped
dash of pepper sauce
6 oz (180 g) avocado (prepared
    weight), thinly sliced

SELECTIONS PER SERVING:

1 Fat
2 Protein
1½ Vegetable
45 Optional Calories

CALORIES PER
SERVING: 275

Flageolet and Cashew Nut Gratinée

SERVES 6
PREPARATION AND COOKING TIME: 25 MINUTES

Put the tomatoes, garlic purée and spring onions into a saucepan, bring to the boil, reduce the heat and simmer uncovered for 4–5 minutes then increase the heat and boil fiercely for 2 minutes.

Process the cashew kernels and bread in a liquidiser or food processor until the bread has formed breadcrumbs. Stir together with the cheese and mix well.

Stir the wine, flageolet beans, artichoke bottoms, smoked ham and a dash of pepper sauce into the tomato mixture, bring to the boil then transfer to a flameproof dish.

Arrange the avocado slices on top of the tomato mixture, sprinkle over the breadcrumb and cheese mixture and cook under a hot grill until golden brown.

Variation:

For a vegetarian meal omit the smoked ham and substitute 6 oz (180 g) smoked tofu. Reduce the Protein Selection to 1½, and add 10 Optional Calories. The Total Calories per serving will be 255.

Flageolet and Cashew Nut Gratinée *illustrated overleaf*

Venison à l'Orange

3 medium oranges
1½ tbs oil
12 × 2 oz (60 g) venison escalopes
1 large clove garlic, finely chopped
2 onions, finely chopped
5 oz (150 g) mushrooms, chopped
3 tbs redcurrant jelly
2 tbs port wine
salt and pepper

SELECTIONS PER SERVING:

½ Fat
½ Fruit
3 Protein
¾ Vegetable
40 Optional Calories

CALORIES PER SERVING: 255

SERVES 6

PREPARATION AND COOKING TIME: 35 MINUTES

Remove a little orange zest from one orange with a zester and set aside. Halve the oranges, reserve a slice from each half, cover with clingfilm and set aside. Squeeze the juice from all the halves.

Heat 1 tablespoon oil in a large frying pan, add six of the escalopes and cook for 50–60 seconds on each side. Transfer the escalopes to a warm plate and repeat with the remaining six escalopes.

Put the remaining oil in the frying pan, stir in the garlic and onions and cook over a moderate heat for about 6 minutes or until golden brown. Add the mushrooms, stir round for 1–2 minutes then add the orange juice.

Stir in the redcurrant jelly and port wine then arrange the venison escalopes on top, season with salt and pepper – don't worry if the escalopes overlap a little, just rearrange them half way through the cooking time. Cover the pan, if it doesn't have a lid lay a large plate on top and cook over a moderate heat for 6 minutes.

While the venison is cooking pour a little boiling water into a saucepan, add the strips of orange zest and boil for 2 minutes, drain and set aside.

Transfer the venison to a warm plate and increase the heat under the frying pan. Boil rapidly for 1–2 minutes. Using a slotted spoon transfer the onion and mushroom mixture to a serving plate and spread evenly. Arrange the venison on top then spoon over the sauce. To serve: scatter on the orange zest and garnish with the slices of orange.

Tip:

This recipe goes well with baby new potatoes, courgettes and carrots or a crisp mixed salad.

Venison à l'Orange *illustrated on previous page*

Sole Fillets with Prawns and Asparagus

1 lb 12 oz (840 g) sole fillets, black skins removed
1 leek or 2 shallots, sliced
slice of lemon
6 fl oz (180 ml) dry white wine
4 fl oz (120 ml) water
small bunch of fresh dill
approximately 24 asparagus tips
1 oz (30 g) margarine
1 oz (30 g) flour
¼ pint (150 ml) whole milk
3 oz (90 g) peeled prawns
6 oz (180 g) seedless white grapes, peeled and halved
lemon juice
salt and pepper
slices or wedges of lemon to garnish

SELECTIONS PER SERVING:

1 Fat
2 Protein
¼ Vegetable
95 Optional Calories

CALORIES PER SERVING: 220

SERVES 6

PREPARATION AND COOKING TIME: 45 MINUTES

Pre-heat the oven to 180°C, 350°F, Gas Mark 4.

Arrange the fish in a rectangular ovenproof dish (if necessary fold the tail ends under the fish so the fillets fit neatly into it). Place the leek or shallots and the lemon slice on top of the fish, pour over the wine and water and add 2 large sprigs of dill. Cover with a piece of foil and bake in the pre-heated oven for 20–25 minutes until cooked.

While the fish is cooking steam the asparagus tips until tender (about 5 minutes).

When the fish is cooked use a fish slice to transfer it to a warm serving plate and pour the cooking liquid into a wide saucepan or frying pan. Bring the liquid to the boil and cook rapidly until reduced to about ¼ pint (150 ml).

Melt the margarine in a small saucepan, add the flour and cook over a low heat for 1 minute stirring all the time. Gradually blend in the milk and the reduced fish cooking liquid and bring to the boil, stirring continuously. Boil for 1–2 minutes. Add the prawns and asparagus and stir for 1–2 minutes then add the grapes and season to taste with a little lemon juice, salt and pepper.

To serve; chop a few sprigs of dill, pour the sauce over the fish and sprinkle with the dill. Garnish with the slices or wedges of lemon. Serve with new potatoes.

Tip One:

To peel the grapes: put them in a pan and just cover with water. Bring to the boil then drain and peel. If you own a microwave oven the grapes can be peeled more easily: place half the grapes in a little wine and cook for about 1 minute then drain and peel, repeat with the remaining grapes.

Tip Two:

For an additional touch of luxury stir 3 tablespoons single cream into the sauce and add 15 Optional Calories per serving. (Total Calories per serving 235.)

3½ tbs oil
juice of 2 lemons
1 tbs chopped fresh coriander
1 tbs chopped fresh chives
salt and pepper
1 lb 2 oz (540 g) skinned and
    boned monkfish
12 scallops (approximately
    1 lb–480 g)
1 red pepper, deseeded and cut
    into 1 inch (2.5 cm) squares
1 yellow pepper, deseeded and
    cut into 1 inch (2.5 cm)
    squares
6 spring onions, halved
3 small courgettes, thickly sliced

SELECTIONS PER SERVING:

1½ Fat
3½ Protein
1¼ Vegetable
10 Optional Calories

CALORIES PER
SERVING: 210

Monkfish and Scallop Kebabs

SERVES 6

PREPARATION AND COOKING TIME: 25 MINUTES PLUS MARINATING

Mix the oil together with the lemon juice, coriander and chives. Season to taste with salt and pepper.

Cut the monkfish into eighteen cubes, place in a non-metallic dish with the scallops and pour over the marinade. Leave to marinate in a cool place for 2 hours or more.

Plunge the red and yellow peppers in boiling water, boil for 3 minutes then drain.

When ready to cook, thread the scallops, monkfish and vegetables on to twelve skewers. Arrange the kebabs on the rack of a grill pan, brush with the marinade and cook for 6–7 minutes turning and basting frequently with the marinade.

Tip:

Any firm-fleshed white fish may be used in place of the monkfish. The kebabs are delicious served with 3 oz (90 g) plain cooked rice and 6 oz (180 g) mixed salad. Remember to add 1 Bread Selection and 2 Vegetable Selections per serving and increase Total Calories per serving to 345.

For the sauce:
2 tbs margarine
9 oz (270 g) leeks, thinly sliced
3 oz (90 g) watercress, roughly
    chopped
6 tbs water
3 tbs single cream
1 tbs lemon juice
salt and pepper
For the salmon:
6 × 5 oz (150 g) salmon steaks
    or cutlets
6 tbs white wine
scant ¼ pint (150 ml) water
lemon slices or wedges and
    sprigs of watercress to
    garnish

Salmon Steaks with Leek and Watercress Sauce

SERVES 6

PREPARATION AND COOKING TIME: 45 MINUTES

Melt the margarine in a saucepan and stir-fry the leeks for about 4 minutes. Add the watercress and stir over a moderate heat for 2 minutes. Add the water, cover and simmer for 15 minutes.

Lay the salmon in a frying pan large enough to hold all the steaks, add the wine and water, cover and simmer over a very low heat for 8–10 minutes. Remove the salmon with a fish slice, transfer to a warm plate, cover and keep warm in a low oven.

SELECTIONS PER SERVING:

1 Fat
4 Protein
¾ Vegetable
30 Optional Calories

CALORIES PER
SERVING: 330

Place the cooked leek and watercress mixture in a liquidiser and process to a purée.

Increase the heat under the salmon cooking liquid and boil fiercely until reduced to about 6 tablespoons liquid. Stir in the leek and watercress purée, add the cream and lemon juice and reheat over a moderate heat, stirring continuously. Season with salt and pepper.

Serve the salmon garnished with the lemon slices or wedges and sprigs of watercress. Serve the sauce separately.

Tip:

The Leek and Watercress Sauce makes a delicious accompaniment to chicken. Replace the reduced fish stock with the same quantity of weak chicken stock.

Right: Salmon Steaks with Leek and Watercress Sauce

Spicy Chicken with Coconut

¾ tsp ground cumin
¼ tsp ground coriander
2 good pinches of hot chilli
   powder
¾ tsp ground ginger
¼ tsp cinnamon
½ tsp turmeric
1 clove garlic, crushed
2 tbs oil
6 × 4 oz (120 g) boned and
   skinned chicken breasts
2 onions, thinly sliced
1 large red pepper, deseeded
   and thinly sliced
1 oz (30 g) creamed coconut,
   grated
6 tbs boiling water
5 fl oz (150 ml) low fat natural
   yogurt

SELECTIONS PER SERVING:

1 Fat
3 Protein
¾ Vegetable
50 Optional Calories

CALORIES PER
SERVING: 245

SERVES 6

PREPARATION AND COOKING TIME: 1 HOUR 30 MINUTES
PLUS 6–7 HOURS MARINATING

Mix the spices and garlic with 1½ tablespoons oil and rub the mixture into the chicken. Leave covered in a cool place for 6–7 hours.

When ready to cook pre-heat the oven to 200°C, 400°F, Gas Mark 6.

Heat the remaining oil in a saucepan and stir-fry the onions and red pepper for 2–3 minutes then cover the saucepan and steam over a low heat for about 12 minutes.

Spoon the onion mixture evenly into a large, shallow ovenproof dish (big enough to hold the chicken in a single layer) and arrange the chicken on top of the onions. Cook, uncovered, in the pre-heated oven for 15 minutes.

Reduce the oven heat to 180°C, 350°F, Gas Mark 4.

Stir the coconut with the hot water in a jug until the coconut has dissolved then blend in the yogurt. Pour over the chicken, cover with foil and bake for 45 minutes.

Tip:

Delicious served with long grain rice to soak up the cooking juices. Allow 3 oz (90 g) cooked rice per serving, add 1 Bread Selection and increase Total Calories per serving to 345.

Chinese Turkey Stir-Fry

1 lb (480 g) boned and skinned
turkey

8 tsps sesame oil

1 large clove garlic, finely
chopped

2 leeks, thinly sliced

1 yellow or red pepper,
deseeded and cut into thin
strips

1 green pepper, deseeded and
cut into thin strips

6 oz (180 g) courgettes, cut into
1½ inch (4 cm) sticks

2 oz (60 g) small mangetout,
topped and tailed

4 oz (120 g) drained canned
bamboo shoots

6 oz (180 g) small water
chestnuts

5 oz (150 g) beansprouts

salt and pepper

1 tsp toasted sesame seeds

soy sauce

SELECTIONS PER SERVING:

2 Fat
3½ Protein
2½ Vegetable
35 Optional Calories

CALORIES PER
SERVING: 280

SERVES 4

PREPARATION AND COOKING TIME: 25 MINUTES

Brush the turkey with a little oil, place on the rack of a grill pan and cook for about 6 minutes, turning once, until it has lost its pinkness and is half-cooked.

Heat the remaining oil in a saucepan, add the garlic and stir over a low heat for 1–2 minutes. Add the leeks and peppers and stir-fry for 3–4 minutes.

Cut the turkey into 1 inch (2.5 cm) cubes, add to the saucepan and stir-fry for a further 3 minutes. Add the courgettes, mangetout, bamboo shoots and water chestnuts, cover and cook over a moderate heat for 4–5 minutes. Add the beansprouts and stir-fry until all the vegetables are piping hot but retain their crunchy texture. Season to taste with salt and pepper.

Transfer to a warm serving dish and sprinkle with the sesame seeds. Serve the soy sauce separately in a small jug.

Tip:

Turkey breasts can be expensive, many supermarkets sell turkey thighs which are more economical.

4 oz (120 g) boned loin pork chop or 3 oz (90 g) cooked pork
5 oz (150 g) long grain rice
6 large peppers each about 7 oz (210 g)
1 tbs oil
1 clove garlic, finely chopped
2 onions, finely chopped
½ tsp ground cumin
½ tsp dried basil
14 oz (420 g) minced turkey
1 tbs vegetable purée
salt and pepper
2 oz (60 g) ready-to-eat dried apricots, roughly chopped
1 oz (30 g) pine kernels or cashew nut kernels, roughly chopped
¾ pint (450 ml) boiling stock

SELECTIONS PER SERVING:

½ Bread
½ Fat
2½ Protein
2½ Vegetable
75 Optional Calories

CALORIES PER SERVING: 285

Peppers Stuffed with Fruity Rice and Nuts

SERVES 6

PREPARATION AND COOKING TIME: 1 HOUR 30 MINUTES

Pre-heat the oven to 190°C, 375°F, Gas Mark 5.

If using uncooked pork place on the rack of a grill pan and cook under a moderate heat, turning once. Leave to cool. Cook the rice according to the packaging instructions.

Cut a very thin slice from the stalk end of each pepper, just enough to be able to cut away the core and remove the seeds. Wash the pepper to remove any remaining seeds. Chop the pepper slices.

Heat the oil in a saucepan, add the garlic, onions, and chopped pepper slices, stir round then cover and cook over a low heat for 6 minutes. Add the cumin and basil then the turkey and stir-fry for 2–3 minutes or until the turkey has lost its pink colour. Then add half the vegetable purée and a generous sprinkling of salt and pepper, cover the saucepan and cook gently for 10–12 minutes.

When cooked stir in the rice, apricots, pork and nuts.

Pack the stuffing firmly into each of the peppers. Stand the peppers upright in an ovenproof dish, stir the boiling stock together with the remaining vegetable purée then pour round the peppers. Cover the dish with foil and cook in the preheated oven for 1 hour. Test the peppers are cooked by piercing with a skewer, if they are cooked the skewer should slide into the pepper skins. Do not overcook or the peppers will lose their attractive colour.

To serve, spoon a little of the cooking liquid over each pepper.

Tip:

To make a really colourful dish use a selection of different coloured peppers, yellow, orange, red and green. The peppers should be able to stand upright but if they lean slightly make sure they are supported during cooking to prevent the stuffing falling out.

Tofu Cakes:
3 oz (90 g) smoked tofu
8 fl oz (240 ml) skimmed milk
10 oz (300 g) self-raising flour
4 tsps baking powder
Cauliflower Sauce:
1 large cauliflower, divided into florets
1 oz (30 g) margarine
1 large onion, finely chopped
1½ oz (45 g) flour
¾ pint (450 ml) skimmed milk
6 oz (180 g) drained canned sweetcorn
4 oz (120 g) soft cheese roulé with garlic and herbs (full fat), cut into small pieces
3 eggs, hard-boiled and roughly chopped
salt and pepper
2 tomatoes, sliced
1 oz (30 g) mature Cheddar or Parmesan cheese, grated

SELECTIONS PER SERVING:

2 Bread
1 Fat
¼ Milk
1½ Protein
2 Vegetable
40 Optional Calories

CALORIES PER
SERVING: 460

Cauliflower au Gratin with Tofu Cakes

SERVES 6

PREPARATION AND COOKING TIME: 45 MINUTES

Pre-heat the oven to 230°C, 450°F, Gas Mark 8.

Make the tofu cakes. Crumble the tofu into a liquidiser, add 6 fl oz (180 ml) skimmed milk and process until no large pieces of tofu remain.

Reserve 1 tablespoon flour and sieve the remainder together with the baking powder into a bowl. Make a well in the centre of the flour and pour the processed tofu and milk into it. Using a round-bladed knife gradually mix to a soft dough adding 3–4 tablespoons milk – don't add too much or the dough will be sticky.

Sprinkle the work surface and rolling pin with the reserved flour and roll out the dough until about ¾ inch (2 cm) thick. Cut into twelve round or triangular cakes.

Lay a piece of non-stick baking parchment on a baking tray, arrange the cakes on top and brush with the remaining milk. Leave to stand for 10–15 minutes then bake in the pre-heated oven for about 12 minutes until golden and well-risen.

While the cakes are standing and baking prepare the cauliflower mixture. Plunge the cauliflower into boiling water and cook for 6 minutes or until just tender, drain well.

Melt the margarine in a saucepan and stir-fry the onion for 5–6 minutes or until transparent. Add the flour and stir well, remove from the heat and gradually blend in the milk. Bring the sauce to the boil, stirring all the time and cook for 2 minutes, stirring continuously. Remove from the heat and stir in the hot drained cauliflower, sweetcorn, soft cheese and eggs and season to taste with salt and pepper. Reheat the sauce then pour into a large rectangular dish. Arrange the hot cakes upright round the sides of the dish, gently press them into the sauce. Arrange the tomato slices on top of the cauliflower sauce, sprinkle over the Cheddar or Parmesan cheese and place under a very hot grill until melted and beginning to brown.

Tip:

This recipe does not reheat well so serve it immediately.

8 oz (240 g) raspberries
6 oz (180 g) strawberries
8 oz (240 g) tayberries
8 oz (240 g) blueberries
1½ tbs caster sugar
4 fl oz (120 ml) sweet white
    wine
6 tbs double cream

SELECTIONS PER SERVING:

1 Fruit
70 Optional Calories

CALORIES PER
SERVING: 120

Four Berry Treat

SERVES 6
PREPARATION: 10 MINUTES PLUS CHILLING
NO COOKING REQUIRED

Reserve a few berries for decoration then process the remainder in a liquidiser until smooth. Add the sugar and wine and process once again.

Pour the fruit purée into six glasses and chill in the refrigerator for 2–3 hours until thick.

Whisk the double cream until thick then spoon it into a piping bag fitted with a ½ inch (1.25 cm) fluted nozzle. Pipe a swirl of cream on top of each fruit purée and decorate with the reserved fruit. Refrigerate until ready to serve.

Tip:

If you are unable to buy all the different berries in the shops the proportions may be changed as long as the total weight – 2 lb (960 g) – remains.

Illustrated on page 214

1 medium mango
4 oz (120 g) cherries, stoned
3 medium apricots, stoned and
    cut into 8 segments
3 medium plums, stoned and cut
    into 8 segments
1 medium banana, cut into thick
    diagonal slices
6 oz (180 g) fresh pineapple,
    sliced
2 tbs frozen concentrated
    orange juice, thawed
1 tsp arrowroot
1½ tbs sugar
4 tbs rum or brandy

SELECTIONS PER SERVING:

1½ Fruit
50 Optional Calories

Fruit Flambé

SERVES 6
PREPARATION AND COOKING TIME: 20 MINUTES

To prepare the mango, cut lengthways along the broadside of the mango, about ½ inch (1.25 cm) away from the centre. Cut through the other side the same distance from the centre, so the long thin stone can be removed. Peel away the skin and cut off the flesh surrounding the stone. Make criss-cross cuts almost through to the skin of each half then turn the outer edge under so the middle of the fruit rises and the cubes of flesh separate. Slide your knife under the cubes and set aside.

Place all the fruit in a flameproof dish or pan. Make the orange juice up to ¼ pint (150 ml) with water. Blend a little of the juice with the arrowroot and set aside.

Sprinkle the sugar over the fruit and simmer gently until the fruit is heated through but retains its shape. Using a draining spoon remove the

CALORIES PER
SERVING: 100

fruit from the dish or pan, increase the heat and boil fiercely for 1–2 minutes. Stir in the arrowroot paste and the remainder of the orange juice and return to the boil, stirring all the time. Boil for 1–2 minutes.

Arrange the hot fruit in a suitable flameproof dish or pan and pour over the boiling syrup. Keep the fruit over a low heat. Warm the rum or brandy. Remove the fruit from the heat, pour over the rum and ignite.

For the roll:
2 large eggs
3 oz (90 g) caster sugar
1 tbs cocoa
1 oz (30 g) plain flour
1 oz (30 g) self-raising flour
1½ tbs warm water
½ tbs caster sugar
For the filling:
6 oz (180 g) fromage frais
½ tbs caster sugar
½ tsp icing sugar
4 oz (120 g) curd cheese
8 oz (240 g) cherries, stoned and halved

SELECTIONS PER SERVING:

½ Protein
115 Optional Calories

CALORIES PER
SERVING: 145

Illustrated on pages 186/187

Black Forest Roll

SERVES 8

PREPARATION AND COOKING TIME: 25 MINUTES PLUS COOLING

Preheat the oven to 220°C, 425°F, Gas Mark 7. Line a Swiss roll tin, approximately 8½ × 12 inch (22 × 30 cm) with non-stick baking parchment.

Break the eggs into a bowl and add 3 oz (90 g) caster sugar. Place the bowl over a saucepan of simmering water and whisk continuously until the mixture is very thick and almost white in colour, about 10 minutes. A trail should be left when the whisk is drawn over the mixture. Continue to whisk off the heat for 2–3 minutes.

Sieve the cocoa and flours twice. Carefully fold the cocoa mixture and warm water into the whisked eggs. Spoon the mixture evenly into the prepared tin, do not spread with a knife or air will be knocked out of the mixture. Bake in the preheated oven for about 9 minutes until the cake springs back when lightly pressed.

While the roll is cooking, dip a cloth about 9 × 12 inch (22.5 × 30 cm) in cold water and wring out tightly. Lay the cloth on a flat working surface and sprinkle with the ½ tbs caster sugar. Cut out a piece of non-stick baking parchment about the same size. Turn the cooked roll out of its tin directly on to the damp cloth. Peel off the lining paper. Cut a very thin strip from each long side of the cake. Mark about 1 inch (2.5 cm) along the length of one of the short edges of the roll, do not cut all the way through the cake. Lay the non-stick baking parchment on top of the roll and, using the cloth, tightly roll the cake up from the marked edge towards the other shorter side. Transfer the roll to a wire rack and leave until cold.

Mix the fromage frais together with the curd cheese. Add the cherries and the caster sugar. Very carefully unroll the cake and spread the filling evenly over it, leaving a gap of about ½ inch (1.25 cm) clear from the edge of the cake. Carefully re-roll the Black Forest Roll and place on a flat serving plate. Sieve the icing sugar over and serve.

Left: Four Berry Treat (page 212)

Right: Strawberry Cheesemousse Cake (page 216)

Left: Pineapple and Kumquat Refresher (page 217)

1 oz (30 g) cornflour
2 oz (60 g) caster sugar
6 oz (180 g) curd cheese
2 eggs, separated
pinch of cream of tartar
4 fl oz (120 ml) double cream
2 oz (60 g) fromage frais (8% fat)
3 tbs strawberry jam
12 oz (360 g) strawberries, thickly sliced

SELECTIONS PER SERVING:

½ Protein
90 Optional Calories

CALORIES PER
SERVING: 145

Illustrated on
page 215

Strawberry Cheesemousse Cake

SERVES 10
PREPARATION AND COOKING TIME: 1 HOUR PLUS COOLING

Pre-heat the oven to 180°C, 350°F, Gas Mark 4.

Line the base and sides of an 8½ inch (21.25 cm) springform tin with non-stick baking parchment.

Mix together the cornflour and sugar.

Beat the curd cheese until smooth, add the egg yolks then blend in the cornflour mixture.

Whisk the egg whites with the cream of tartar until peaking. Gently fold into the curd cheese mixture then pour into the prepared tin.

Bake in the pre-heated oven for 30 minutes. When cooked leave in the cake tin to cool – the cake will sink until about 1 inch (2.5 cm) thick.

Just before serving whisk the double cream until it holds its own shape, stir in the fromage frais. Place the cake on a serving plate and spread the creamy mixture over the top and down the sides of the cake.

Place the jam in a cup or small basin and stand in a saucepan of simmering water until it begins to thin. Leave until cool but still runny. Add the strawberries and stir to coat all the fruit. Remove the strawberries one at a time and use to decorate the top of the cake. Arrange any remaining strawberries round the edge of the serving plate.

Tip:

Make this delicious cake during the summer when strawberries are in season and full of flavour.

4 tsps oil
1 tbs honey
1 oz (30 g) barley flakes
1 oz (30 g) wheat flakes
½ oz (15 g) flaked almonds
4 tbs custard powder
1 pint (600 ml) skimmed milk
1 tbs sugar
few drops vanilla essence
4 medium bananas, thickly sliced

Banana Custard with Crunchy Topping

SERVES 4
PREPARATION AND COOKING TIME: 20 MINUTES

Heat the oil and honey in a small saucepan, add the barley and wheat flakes and stir well. Remove from the heat and mix in the flaked almonds.

SELECTIONS PER SERVING:

½ Bread
1 Fat
2 Fruit
½ Milk
80 Optional Calories

CALORIES PER
SERVING: 305

Spread the flakes and nuts thinly and evenly over the base of a grill pan and cook under a low to moderate grill, stirring occasionally until a deep golden colour. Remove from the heat and leave to cool.

Blend the custard powder with a little of the milk, heat the remainder in a saucepan. Stir the custard powder into the steaming milk and bring to the boil stirring all the time. Boil for 2 minutes. Add the sugar and vanilla essence.

Stir the bananas into the custard and cook over a low heat for 1–2 minutes – just enough to heat the bananas. Spoon the custard into serving dishes and sprinkle with the crunchy topping. Serve immediately.

Variation:

If preferred this recipe could be served cold. Leave the custard to cool, then just before serving stir in the sliced bananas and sprinkle with the topping. Do not sprinkle the topping over and leave to cool or it will lose its crunchy texture.

---

1 oz (30 g) sugar
6 fl oz (180 ml) water
thin strip of lemon zest
½–1 tsp orange flower water
large sprig of mint
20 medium kumquats, halved
10 oz (300 g) fresh pineapple, cubed

SELECTIONS PER SERVING:

1 Fruit
45 Optional Calories

CALORIES PER
SERVING: 115

Pineapple and Kumquat Refresher

SERVES 4
PREPARATION AND COOKING TIME: 15 MINUTES PLUS COOLING

Place the sugar, water and lemon zest in a small saucepan and heat gently until the sugar has dissolved, increase the heat and boil fiercely for 1½ minutes. Remove the saucepan from the heat and stir in the orange flower water and mint.

Arrange the fruit in a bowl, pour over the hot syrup and leave until cool. Remove the lemon zest and mint before serving.

Tip:

Orange flower water can be purchased at chemists, delicatessens or large supermarkets.

Illustrated on page 214

Vanilla and Apricot Pancake Layer Pudding

For the pancakes:
4 oz (120 g) plain flour
pinch of salt
1 egg
½ pint (300 ml) skimmed milk
1 tbs oil
For the almond layer:
1 oz (30 g) flaked almonds
4 tbs apricot jam
For the apricot sauce:
1 lb 4 oz (600 g) drained canned
**   apricots (approximately**
**   2 medium cans)**
2 tbs frozen concentrated
**   orange juice, thawed**
artificial sweetener
For the vanilla sauce:
2 oz (60 g) cornflour
1 pint (600 ml) skimmed milk
¼–½ tsp vanilla essence
1–2 tsps lemon juice
artificial sweetener

SELECTIONS PER SERVING:

1 Bread
½ Fat
1 Fruit
½ Milk
½ Protein
40 Optional Calories

CALORIES PER
SERVING: 275

SERVES 6

PREPARATION AND COOKING TIME: 1 HOUR 30 MINUTES

To make the pancakes: sieve the flour and salt into a bowl, make a well in the centre, add the egg and gradually beat or whisk in the milk. Set aside.

Prove a small frying pan; generously sprinkle salt over the base of the frying pan, heat gently, tip out the salt then wipe thoroughly with a pad of kitchen paper. Heat a small amount of oil in the pan and wipe once again.

Heat about ¼ teaspoon oil in the pan, pour in a little batter whilst turning the pan so it coats the base. Cook over a moderate heat until the underside is golden, toss or turn over and cook the other side. Tip on to a plate and keep warm while continuing the procedure to make 12 pancakes.

Spread the flaked almonds on to a baking sheet and place in the oven while it heats up to 180°C, 350°F, Gas Mark 4. They should be an even, light golden brown colour.

Place the apricots and orange juice in a liquidiser and process to a purée. Add artificial sweetener equivalent to ¾ oz (20 g) sugar.

Blend the cornflour to a smooth paste with a little milk. Heat the remaining milk until steaming then stir in the cornflour and bring to the boil stirring all the time. Boil for 1–2 minutes. Add ¼ teaspoon vanilla essence, 1 teaspoon lemon juice and sweeten to taste with artificial sweetener. Add a little more lemon juice and vanilla essence if desired.

Assemble the pancake layers. Place one pancake in the base of an ovenproof dish, spread with a little of the apricot purée and cover with a pancake. Spread a quarter of the vanilla sauce over then top with another pancake and a layer of apricot purée. Reserve a few almond flakes for decoration.

Lay a pancake on top of the apricot purée and spread it with 2 tablespoons of jam then sprinkle with half the nuts, cover with a pancake and repeat the layers once again. Continue layering the apricot purée, pancakes and vanilla sauce ending with a layer of vanilla sauce.

Cook the pancake layers in the pre-heated oven for 40–45 minutes, sprinkle with the reserved flaked almonds and serve.

Tip:

If you wish to prepare this in advance make the pancakes, apricot sauce and vanilla sauce and freeze separately in suitable containers.

Top: Orange and Yogurt Mousse (page 220)

Bottom: Peach Eclairs (page 220)

Orange Yogurt Mousse

16 fl oz (480 ml) orange juice
1 oz (30 g) caster sugar
1½ tbs gelatine
4 tbs frozen concentrated
    orange juice, thawed
10 fl oz (300 ml) low fat natural
    yogurt

SELECTIONS PER SERVING:

1½ Fruit
½ Milk
30 Optional Calories

CALORIES PER
SERVING: 140

SERVES 4

PREPARATION AND COOKING TIME: 5 MINUTES
PLUS COOLING AND SETTING

Heat 4 fl oz (120 ml) of the orange juice, pour into a bowl and sprinkle in the caster sugar and gelatine, stir well and leave until dissolved. If necessary stand the bowl in a saucepan of simmering water.

Mix the remaining orange juice and concentrated orange juice together then stir in the dissolved gelatine. Chill until almost set.

Whisk the setting jelly well then gradually whisk in the yogurt. Pour into four serving glasses and chill until set.

Tip:

Substitute the gelatine with a vegetable based gelling agent when preparing this recipe for vegetarians.

Illustrated on page 219

Peach Eclairs

For the choux pastry:
3 tbs water
4 tsps margarine
1 oz (30 g) strong white bread
    flour
1 egg, beaten
For the filling:
1 medium peach, stoned and
    chopped
½ tsp lemon juice
3 oz (90 g) curd cheese
3 oz (90 g) fromage frais
1 tbs caster sugar
For the topping:
4 tsps chocolate spread

SELECTIONS PER SERVING:

1 Fat
1 Protein
75 Optional Calories

SERVES 4

PREPARATION AND COOKING TIME: 45 MINUTES

Pre-heat the oven to 200°C, 400°F, Gas Mark 6.

Line a baking sheet with non-stick baking parchment.

Gently heat the water and margarine in a very small saucepan until the margarine has melted. Increase the heat and bring to a rolling boil. Add the flour all at once, beat well and cook over a moderate heat for a few seconds. Allow to cool a little and then gradually add the egg, beating well after each addition, until the paste is smooth and glossy.

Spoon the pastry into a piping bag fitted with a plain ¾ inch (2 cm) nozzle. Pipe into four 3–3½ inch (7.5–8.75 cm) lengths.

Place in the pre-heated oven and immediately increase the heat to 220°C, 425°F, Gas Mark 7 and bake for 25 minutes. Make a slit in each éclair to allow the steam to escape and return to the oven for a further 4–5 minutes. Cool on a wire rack.

CALORIES PER
SERVING: 175

Not more than an hour before serving, toss the peach in the lemon juice. Mix together the curd cheese, fromage frais and sugar and stir in the chopped peach.

Cut horizontally right through each eclair, spoon the filling mixture on to the bottom half and cover with the top half.

Spoon the chocolate spread into a cup and stand in a saucepan of simmering water until just warm. Spread on the top of each eclair.

Tip:

Illustrated on page 219

Strong breadmaking flour helps the choux pastry to hold its shape.

---

3 large eggs, separated
4 oz (120 g) caster sugar
grated zest and juice of
**   2 lemons**
2 tbs hot water
1 sachet gelatine
6 oz (180 g) fromage frais (8%
**   fat)**
1 egg white
pinch of cream of tartar
4 tsps desiccated coconut,
**   toasted if desired**
lemon slices to garnish

SELECTIONS PER SERVING:

1 Protein
90 Optional Calories

CALORIES PER
SERVING: 155

Illustrated on page 103

Chilled Lemon Soufflé

SERVES 6
PREPARATION AND COOKING TIME: 30 MINUTES
PLUS COOLING AND SETTING

Put the egg yolks into a large mixing bowl with the caster sugar, the grated lemon zest and lemon juice. Stand the bowl over a saucepan of simmering water and whisk until the mixture is pale in colour and thick. The whisk should leave a trail of mixture when lifted.

Pour the 2 tablespoons hot water into a cup or small basin, sprinkle in the gelatine and stir. Stand the cup in a saucepan of simmering water until the gelatine has dissolved.

Continue whisking the lemon mixture off the heat for 2–3 minutes. Stir in the dissolved gelatine and leave until beginning to set.

Secure a band of non-stick baking parchment round the sides of a 6 inch (15 cm) soufflé dish, leave the paper about 1½ inch (4 cm) above the height of the dish.

Stir the fromage frais into the thick lemon mixture.

Whisk all the egg whites (including the additional one) with the cream of tartar until peaking. Using a metal spoon fold the egg whites into the lemon mixture. Spoon into the prepared dish and chill until completely set.

Carefully remove the non-stick paper from the dish and press the coconut on to the sides of the soufflé. Just before serving decorate with the lemon slices.

Index

Index

As many materials and techniques are used throughout the book, the page references are intended to direct the reader to substantial entries only. Page numbers in *italics* refer to illustrations.